F U N

FOR THE FAMILY

FUN
FOR THE FAMILY

Compiled and Edited by

JEROME S. MEYER

Author of *Mind Your P's and Q's,*
Mental Whoopee, Snap Judgment, etc., etc.
Puzzle Editor of *College Humor*

Garden City   New York

GARDEN CITY PUBLISHING CO., INC.

1939
GARDEN CITY PUBLISHING CO., INC.

Copyright, 1937, by
GREENBERG, PUBLISHER, INC.
67 West 44th Street   New York

CL

PRINTED IN THE UNITED STATES OF AMERICA

ACKNOWLEDGMENT

I want to express my sincere appreciation and gratitude to the authors of the following books, magazine editors, publishers and others for their permissions and valuable contributions to this book:

COLLEGE HUMOR MAGAZINE for permission to use many of my Mental Merry-Go-Round Puzzles.

GERALD LYNTON KAUFMAN, author and amateur magician, for his section of Time Sequence and many Tricks, Stunts and Action Games.

DOUBLEDAY, DORAN & CO. for permission to use excerpts from the following Heyday House publications:

It's About Time by *Gerald Kaufman*
Bringing Sherlock Home by *Lawrence Treat*
Naming Quintuplets by *J. Bryan III*
May I Leave the Room? by *G. Kendall*

LAWRENCE TREAT for his section on Picture Murder Clues and J. BRYAN III for his Name Five puzzles.

SIMON AND SCHUSTER for permission to use excerpts from the Anagram Book by Silas Seadler and Mathemagic by Royal Vale Heath.

ROYAL HEATH, JUSTIN KIRK, MILTON GOLDSMITH and MABEL MEYER for Mathemagic, Double Crosswords, Anagram Puzzles and other contributions.

J. S. M.

THE ANSWERS

or solutions to all problems, puzzles and tests will be found in Part IX starting on page 243. Many of the puzzles and games in this book require written answers. These should be done on separate pieces of paper in order not to mar the volume. Remember, the rest of the family will want to use the book, too.

CONTENTS

Fun to be Fold — High Finance — Full Name Please —
College Men's Golden Rule — A Weighty Problem —
Quintuplets on the Square — Not so Easy — On the
Square — Between the Lines — It's Easy When You
Know How — Too Much Is Enough.

Baseball — I Know You — Spooning Contest — Get Rid
of the Orange — Folding Chair Relay Race — Ping
Pong Football — Whistle-Cracker.

A WORD TO THE READER

FUN FOR THE FAMILY has been carefully designed to appeal to everyone in your family. Unlike any other book, it includes puzzles and problems which can be done alone. These puzzles, or brain twisters, will appeal particularly to father, who will love to solve the Detective Mystery Pictures and test his ability in observation and memory. Father will also like the two tests of mechanical imagination, the District Attorney problems, and the Sense of Time puzzles, which are entirely original. If he happens to be of a more literary turn of mind, he will like also to do the anagrams and word puzzles.

Mother will certainly love these word puzzles. She will be particularly keen on the special tests and general information quizzes. Of course Mother is just as much of a hostess as her daughter and they can both romp to their hearts' content through the hundred odd games included. Mother can select hers for the older people and daughter can take the more peppy games for her crowd.

The games are for the most part not new. Many old favorites have been included because they have stood the test of time and always come out with flying colors. Of course there are a great many original games in this section—games that have never before been published—which we know are sure to provide a great deal of fun and amusement. This part is really for the hostess, whether she be 18 or 81. In it you will find a great diversity of games and you never need worry again what to do with the crowd.

Then, of course, there is Junior. He is an extremely im-

xi

portant part of the family. He will love the stunts and tricks in magic and it won't be long before he will know every one of them and be amazing his friends with his new-found hobby. The many stunts, tricks and magic included have been carefully selected from the numerous ideas and papers submitted. A great many of them came from Mr. Gerald Kaufman, a brilliant amateur magician and member of the Society of American Magicians.

Of course our predictions may be all askew: Father might go in strong for the magic and Junior might tackle the anagrams and word puzzles. Mother on the other hand might like the District Attorney and murder problems and daughter might be fascinated by the Mechanical Imagination pictures. If this happens it's all the same to us. We can predict only one thing and that is FUN FOR THE FAMILY really will be fun for the family and every member of it. So, no matter who you are in the family, we are sure you will enjoy this book. It is a compilation of the best material that we have been able to find, edited and compiled by a well known authority in the field of entertainment, who not only has written many books on puzzles and games and edited puzzle pages for magazines, but who organized and conducted a special game department for one of the largest publishing houses in the country, through which he was able to obtain some of the most original and fascinating material.

THE PUBLISHERS

Part I

WORD PUZZLES
AND
ANAGRAMS

BOXWORD PUZZLES

Fill in the twenty-five squares in each of the diagrams with the twenty-five letters given under each diagram, in such a way as to make as many five letter words as you can, horizontally and vertically. If you can't get five letter words, get four letter words—but get as many words as you can. The scoring is as follows:

five letter words count 10
four letter words count 5
three letter words count 0

A score of 50 is fair, 60 is good, 70 is very good, 80 is excellent, and 95 is perfect.

I

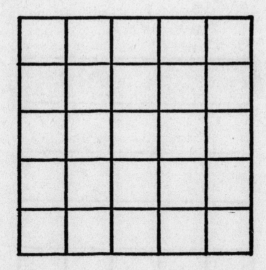

L E T I C A L G E S R S
D E S M I E O A E I S D E

2

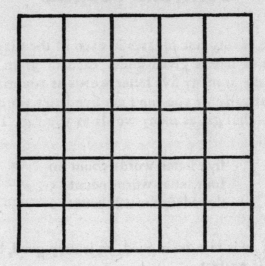

A I C A E H O T D S T A R

S C R E P V L E I N T E

3

I D Y L R S R E T N A S

T R E O E R T F A A N P I

CONNECTOGRAMS

Fill in each numbered space in the following diagrams which fits the definition opposite its corresponding number in the definitions and is also commonly associated with the word which precedes it, follows it, and is directly below it.

For example, suppose one of the words were "shower." Suppose the definition of the preceding word were "fourth month." Obviously the word we are looking for is "April," since "April" fits the definition and also is associated with "shower"—"April shower" is a common expression. Now suppose the definition of the word in the space below "April" were "A simpleton." The correct word is therefore "Fool," because "April fool" is a common expression. The Connectogram is a continuous pairing of words, both vertically and horizontally—the last word in the pair is always the first word in the following pair—and the pairs of words always go together. In the case illustrated, we might have something like the following:

APRIL	SHOWER	BATH	HOUSE	BOAT
FOOL		ROOM		TRIP
PROOF		MATE		UP

You will note that each pair of words is associated with the other pair and that they run right along continuously. It is up to you to fill in the diagram in this fashion. The numbers in the spaces refer to the numbers in the definitions. Some definitions have been omitted intentionally. Compound words like fool-proof, bellhop and understand, etc. are considered two words.

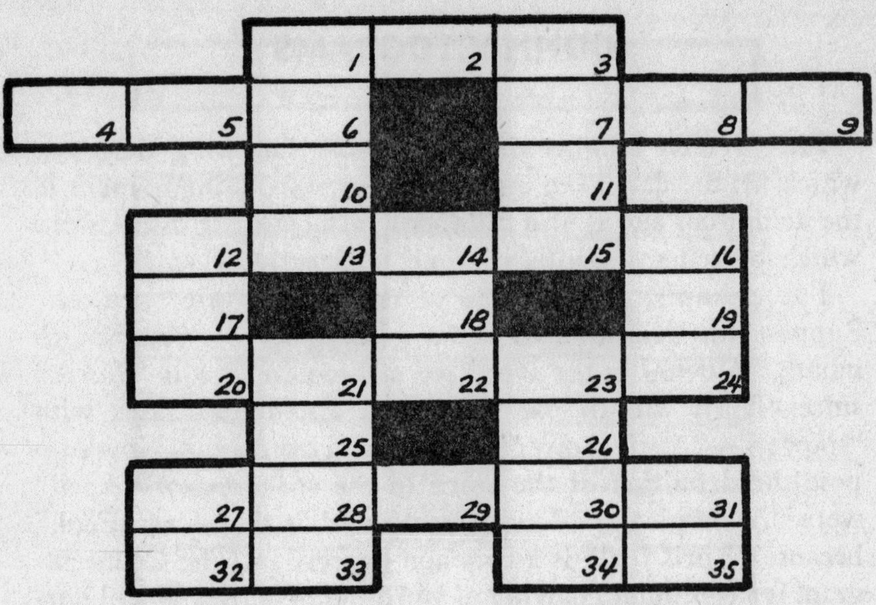

Definitions

1. Exalted
2. Musical drama
3. Manage
4. Female gander
5. A pace
6. Female parent
7. Bound volume
8. Coat with metal electrically
9. Mirror
10.
11.
12. Large body of water
13. Ill
14. Piece of furniture
15. Period of duration
16. Time piece
17.
18. Room
19. Labor
20. Potential capacity
21.
22. Young girl
23. Act of serving
24. Store
25. Retain
26.
27. Cease moving
28. Preposition
29. Small City
30.
31. Direction
32. Above
33. Revolve
34. Regard or heed
35. Below

	1	2	3	4	5
		6	■		7
	8	9	■	10	11
	12	13	14	15	16
	17	■	18	■	19
	20	21	22	23	24
	25	26	■	27	28
		29	■	30	
	31	32	33	34	35

Definitions

1. Affording free ingress
2. A store
3.
4. Opposite to in
5. To throw out
6. Labor
7. An edge
8. Vapor
9.
10.
11. Female child
12. Cooking apparatus
13. Long tube of metal
14.
15. A young female
16.
17. Rasp
18. A realm
19. To conquer
20. Rapid combustion
21. A fluid
22. To note
23. Period of duration
24. A timepiece
25. Insect
26.
27. A portion
28. Labor
29. A tuft of hair
30.
31. A pace
32. Preposition
33. Pawn
34.
35. An active cause

Definitions

1. A prefix meaning against
2. Companionable
3. A heavy stick
4.
5. Not fastened
6. A narrow passageway
7. The upper bony part of the nose
8. To do business with
9. A visible sign
10.
11. A piece of furniture
12. A woven fabric
13. Preposition
14.
15. Part of the leg
16. Exalted, lofty
17. To throw
18. Total darkness
19.
20. Extending far below the surface
21. Not light
22. Production of one who writes
23.
24. The ocean
25. A domestic animal
26. An insect
27. What this puzzle is printed on
28.
29. A vehicle
30. A disc used for locomotion
31. A plank
32.
33. A fastening
34. A pace

DOUBLE CROSSWORDS

Directions for Each Puzzle

Insert the word indicated by definition number 1. Just add the correct letter to the word, rearrange the letters, and you have the answer to definition number 2.—Then drop the correct letter from number 1, rearrange the remaining letters, and you get the word called for by definition number 3. That's all there is to it.—Repeat for each group of three words.

Print the letters added and dropped in the vertical columns on the left and right respectively. These letters are of help in a pinch—and productive of one or more interesting sidelights. Clues to these sidelights are contained in the puzzle captions.

Two prepositions will be seen to result from this EXAMPLE:—

	2 TO GIVE CHARITABLY	1 FAMED; ILLUSTRIOUS	3 IS FINISHED	
A	D O N A T E	N O T E D	D O N E	T
	5 REMOVAL PROCEDURE	4 TO AWAKE WITH A START	6 CERTAIN; POSITIVE	
T	O U S T E R	R O U S E	S U R E	O

When in Competition

Score ONE point for the person or partnership first to insert or declare a word.—Score THREE points for the person or partnership first to insert or declare a sidelight.—Numerical order can be disregarded.—It is a free-for-all from start to finish—with nimble double-crossers piling up points from your desire to disclose too soon; or delay too long. So beware.

EMINENT STATESMEN

Here will be revealed two of the nation's most eminent statesmen, who reigned before the dawn of the New Deal. Vote either ticket. But all returns should be in at the end of 21 minutes.

2 A DEAD BODY	1 WITHIN THE RANGE OF	3 TO SIT FOR A PICTURE
5 TO BESEECH	4 A WRINKLE IN CLOTH	6 THE FIRST; ORIGINAL
8 COOKED BY HEAT	7 OCCUPATIONS	9 POINTED WEAPONS
11 A SERF; DRUDGE	10 FLESH OF CALF	12 ALCOHOLIC BEVERAGE
14 A MARK LEFT BY PRESSING	13 FARM LAND MEASURES	15 MARK LEFT BY A WOUND
17 DIVULGES; DISCLOSES	16 A TYPE OF FISHERMAN	18 TO RUB OUT
20 ENGAGED IN PERUSING	19 FEARLESS; BOLD; BRAVE	21 TO SHARPEN SCISSORS
23 GAINS KNOWLEDGE	22 MORE RATIONAL	24 HEARING ORGANS
26 TO ABANDON	25 MUSICAL PIPES	27 A PROPHET

COME INTO COURT

Come into Court. And bear witness to these two people, who very seldom agree. Perhaps you'll concur. In any case, the verdict should be in at the end of 27 minutes.

2 IN UTTER LOSS OF HOPE	1 TO DESIRE EAGERLY	3 TO LIFT UP; TO ELEVATE
5 PURIFIED BY STRAINING	4 TREATED THINGS LIGHTLY	6 SPLIT APART
8 PUFFS UP WITH AIR	7 VERY PROMINENT	9 WAS MUTE; SPEECHLESS
11 INCIDENTAL NARRATIVE	10 WELL BALANCED	12 GIVES DRUGS TO
14 A HARD MUSCLE CHORD	13 TUNED	15 TO BE SILLY THRU AGE
17 TO MAKE BELIEVE	16 TO BE SORRY FOR SOMETHING	18 TO TRIM THE FEATHERS
20 OPTICAL ILLUSION	19 DIRT	21 DISEASE SPREADER
23 AUTOMOBILE BUMPER	22 WAS LIBERATED	24 FAST ANIMAL
26 A SLENDER THREAD; FIBER	25 TO SET ON FIRE; PROVOKE	27 A LOW DOMESTIC SERVANT

SAME LETTER ANAGRAMS

In each of the verses the letters indicated by the dashes are the same and must be transposed to make sense. The number of dashes indicate the number of letters in the words, for example, in the first verse the first word is PRIEST and the second word is STRIPE. What are the other words in this verse and in the other verses?

TO the — — — — — — who had a — — — — — — of red
Came a girl like a — — — — — — — who laughingly said:
"I'll give you a bowl of the — — — — — — beans
If you'll tell what the French word — — — — — — means!"

Said a fond husband to his — — — —
"My dear, as a — — — — — we are surely first rate.
But our diet is — — — — and so we shall eat
A little more fruit and a great deal more — — — —!"

The doctor shook his — — — — — white head
He stroked his — — — — — — and sadly said:
"Though — — — — — and oatmeal you may eat
You must — — — — — rich food and meat!"

A fox across the — — — — — — flees;
The hunter — — — — — after it.
He — — — — — not for a life of ease
He does not — — — — — — a bit.
He falls and gives his foot a wrench . . . .
— — — — —! he says in perfect French.

Although it is only a — — — — —
It could — — — — plenty of light.
It's an — — — — to own and to prime
and a priceless possession in — — — —

UNTRANSPOSED ANAGRAMS

In the following the words are used in various ways *without transposing the order of the letters*. Although they are not true anagrams they are very interesting, for they show how words may be divided. The words may be divided into two parts, the second part being frequently used *ahead* of the first part. See how many you can do: Number 1 has been done for you.

1. In spite of his 87 years the A G E D M A N still M A N A G E D —————————— to attend to his business.
2. Her ——————————— told her that ———————— —— —— —— a convent was best for her sister.
3. The vigilant ——————————— took the ————, ————— and other booty to the police station.
4. This ————— ———— is one whose sympathy for ——————— knows no bounds.
5. Her mother said "I would really ————— ———— about your personal appearance if you were not so ————————— about money matters!"
6. The show commences at quarter —— ———— but it is ————— as much as half an hour late.
7. He was accused of ————————————— but the other ———— ——————————— won him a verdict of acquittal.
8. The optician found that in order to ————— ———— right he had to ——————— his glasses.
9. It was the ———————— for shad but with such high ———— —— he wouldn't dare take a chance with his little boat.
10. In 1776 the patriots indulged in fervid ———————— and at times it was difficult to tell whether a man were a whig —— — —————

SAME WORD—DIFFERENT MEANINGS

It all depends upon how you say it or how you write it in a sentence. This is shown by the following eight sentences. They all contain pairs of words which look the same but are pronounced and used differently. See how many of these words you can fill in. Number 1 has been done for you.

1. He, as a S U B J E C T of a foreign land, will S U B- J E C T our people to many dangers if he enters here with his propaganda.
2. I would _ _ _ _ _ _ _ this manifesto to him if I knew his correct _ _ _ _ _ _ _.
3. An — — — — — — — — of the penal law declares that he may not _ _ _ _ _ _ _ _ any property belonging to the firm.
4. The _ _ _ _ _ _ _, knowing that she was beyond hope wished to make her will, but it would have been _ _ _ _ _ _ _ on account of her mental condition.
5. In _ _ _ _ _ _ _ to the thief it would be well to remember that what he stole was _ _ _ _   _ _ _ _ and not worth a cent.
6. In playing _ _ _ _ _ _ _ _, it is well to keep silent or to _ _ _ _ _ _ _ _ your speech as much as possible.
7. The skipper cried to his daughter "_ _ _ _   _ _ _ _ _ or the cord will slip and the _ _ _ _ _ _ _ _ will be lost overboard!"
8. The fool who wanders into trackless _ _ _ _ _ _ _ _, who loses his way and is overcome by the heat, only gets his just _ _ _ _ _ _ _.

PROGRESSIVE ANAGRAM VERSES

After finding the synonym for the capitalized word in one verse, add a letter and get the word which is wanted in the next verse, and so on, always adding a letter and transposing the letters to get a new word. The article in the first verse, for example, is AN and when P is added we get PAN (a synonym for DISH which is capitalized). Now, go on from there:

Put P before an ARTICLE
And get a kitchen DISH.
But daughter doesn't want to cook
She has a higher wish.

She yearns to study music
And through the rhythm step,
She adds an S,—a word she spells
That means the same as PEP.

With I she forms a word that shows
The TROUBLE that she took,
When practicing her exercises
In her music book.

With O she found the INSTRUMENTS
On which she likes to play.
For nothing could dispel her zeal;
She practiced night and day.

Another S will form a word
That proves her EAGERNESS.
And we predict that so much zeal
Will surely bring success.
The words are:
A N   P A N   _ _ _ _   _ _ _ _ _

_ _ _ _ _ _ _ _ _ _ _ _

TRANSPOSITIONS

Here are some very good Anagrams. They all can be turned into words which are particularly appropriate. See how many you can get:

1. Transpose IT'S IN CHARITY and get a religion:
   _ _ _ _ _ _ _ _ _ _ _ _

2. Transpose GOLDEN LAND and get the country that it best describes: _ _ _ _ _ _ _ _ _ _

3. Transpose BEST IN PRAYER and get another religion:
   _ _ _ _ _ _ _ _ _ _ _ _

4. Transpose NO MORE STARS and get students of stars:
   _ _ _ _ _ _ _ _ _ _

5. Transpose NAY, I REPENT IT and get the place where it is enforced: _ _ _ _ _ _ _ _ _ _ _ _

6. Transpose GO PASS TEN and get what makes cars do it: _ _ _ _ _ _ _ _ _

7. Transpose GREAT HELP and get the instrument that is a great help: _ _ _ _ _ _ _ _ _

8. Transpose BUD AT TEENS and get another name for it: _ _ _ _ _ _ _ _ _

9. Transpose A DOG'S LIFE and get what it is:
   _ _ _ _ _ _ _ _ _

10. Transpose LURES FOR ME and get the feeling you have after being lured: _ _ _ _ _ _ _ _ _ _

11. Transpose RECEIVED PAYMENT and get another way of saying it:
    _ _ _ _ _ _ _ _ _ _ _ _ _ _

NONSENSE ANAGRAM VERSE

Here is some real meangingless patter for you. The words are real words but the letters are all mixed up. Try to unscramble these and make sense out of verse. Some of the words need no unscrambling—but that is up to you:

desiBe the mearsletst ginshin nabd
The nishefrma tas lal dya.
noAn he dresai a zayl ahdn
To vired a tnag away.
teY hothug he was me dinstang by,
he vage no douwart sing
tuB pekt his neke and futchwal yee
ponU sih rednels line.

ADDITION ANAGRAMS

Add the words as indicated and get what you are told to get. Number 1, for example, is log-book.

1. Add a trunk of a fallen tree and a novel and get a sailor's bible.

2. Add "spying" and a drinking vessel and get what every woman looks at most.

3. Add a great bulk and a plot of land and get a terrible slaughter.

4. Add a useful feature of your coat and a literary volume and get a much needed article, especially when filled.

5. Add a cube of wood and the chief end of man's anatomy, and get a stupid fellow.

6. Add the symbols of ten and fifty and get what every boy should want to do.

7. Add angry to a verbal effort and get a popular kind of puzzle.

8. Add judgment to ability and get what sensible people are expected to be at all times.

9. Add a famous Christmas berry to what trees are made of and get a well known city.

10. Add a fruit to a Shepherd dog and get downcast.

HIDDEN GEOGRAPHY

Here are some sentences within which are hidden the names of rivers, cities and countries. See if you can find them, and underline them. No. 1 has been done—it is NILE.

1. Did you see the man I left behind? He was a powerful Arab. (*a river*)

2. I went to London with a messenger who returned as soon as I was through with my business there. (*a river*)

3. The gang established its headquarters on the banks of the river, but the police found their lair. (*a river*)

4. I often wonder how can a damsel make such a display of herself. (*a dominion*)

5. Will Anna polish the silver for the party? (*a city*)

6. Tell Carmen I anticipate a visit from her this evening. (*a country*)

7. Unfortunately the sale might have been avoided if the mortgage had been paid. (*a city*)

8. It is not rich art Ford wants, but antiques of bygone days. (*a city*)

9. Her ma consented to her going to the concert with me. (*a city*)

10. She tries to please in every way, but she cannot cook. (*a river*)

11. Boy, was I a sucker? (*a continent*)

12. Model a War each year. (*a State*)

13. How much I lend you depends on me. (*a republic*)

14. Did you ever try to color a doughnut? (*a State*)

15. The circle was eighteen feet in diameter. (*a country*)

16. Grandma, I never eat spinach! (*a State*)

17. Things being such I naturally want to go. (*a country*)

18. The liqueur operators are all racketeers. (*a continent*)

19. Certainly we agree, Certainly! (*a country*)

20. That ham is sour, I am sure. (*a State*)

STRAIGHTEN THEM OUT

These sentences certainly need straightening out and it is up to you to do it in the quickest possible time. Remember that each sentence begins with a capital letter and there is a period after the last letter in each case. This will immediately fix the first and last words for you and you can go on from there. Here are the ten sentences:

1. body the of 98.6 The degrees. temperature is

....

2. America. city New the is in York largest

....

3. kittens dogs cats. and into grow Puppies into

....

4. mountain is the world. the in Everest peak Mt. highest

....

5. all Beethoven greatest. the Of the was composers

....

6. plus The 3 product the sum of sixes of 6 threes is the sum of 6 and 6.

....

7. A father. his uncle but his man never be older may be can than than older

....

8. intellect is to-day, a professor in Albert the most in Princeton. world brilliant Einstein, the

....

9. public duty on his do spirited Every by jury. will citizen serving a

....

10. Ohio is not but Cincinnati is the capital capital the of Indiana. of Indianapolis

....

SAME IS DIFFERENT

See how many words you can get out of the word SAME by the addition of the letters given.

S A M E with B _ _ _ _ _
S A M E with D _ _ _ _ _
S A M E with G _ _ _ _ _
S A M E with L (two words) _ _ _ _ _ _ _ _ _ _ _
S A M E with N _ _ _ _ _
S A M E with R (three words) _ _ _ _ _ _ _ _ _ _ _
_ _ _ _ _
S A M E with S _ _ _ _ _
S A M E with T _ _ _ _ _
S A M E with U _ _ _ _ _

HOW ABOUT SABRE?

How many words can you get out of the word SABRE by addition of the letters given?

S A B R E with C _ _ _ _ _ _
S A B R E with D (two words) _ _ _ _ _ _ _ _
_ _ _ _
S A B R E with I (two words) _ _ _ _ _ _ _ _
_ _ _ _
S A B R E with K (two words) _ _ _ _ _ _ _ _
_ _ _ _
S A B R E with L _ _ _ _ _ _
S A B R E with T _ _ _ _ _ _
S A B R E with V _ _ _ _ _ _
S A B R E with Z _ _ _ _ _ _

EAT YOUR WORDS

See how many words you can make out of the word ATE by the addition of the letters given. There are 30 words. How many can you find?

ATE with B (3 words) ....

ATE with D (1 word) ....

ATE with F (2 words) ....

ATE with G (1 word) ....

ATE with H (2 words) ....

ATE with L (2 words) ....

ATE with M (4 words) ....

ATE with N (4 words) ....

ATE with P (3 words) ....

ATE with R (3 words) ....

ATE with S (5 words) ....

Part II

50

BRAIN

TWISTERS

(Arranged in Order of Difficulty)

---

1. A COCK-EYED STORY

(Par: 5 min.)

The story given below contains thirteen commonly used expressions—expressions like "fresh air fiend," "butter-and-egg man," etc. These expressions, which are in italics, are all mixed up, as you will see when you read the story. It's up to you to straighten them out and list them in their correct order on a piece of paper.

When Arthur Ables announced his marriage, it came as a big surprise to his friends who had always believed him to be a *absent-minded father,* and it did seem odd to watch him lead his *tired idiot* away after the marriage ceremony. But it was no surprise, a year later, to hear that he was a *blithering nuisance* of a *crooked bachelor!*

And how happy he was at the *blushing citizen!* He went around acting like a *new-born general* and making a *traveling bride* of himself! Being a *baby business man* for a large wholesale house, he managed to spread the news all over the country. The *proud politicians* considered him a *public-spirited tire* and in one of the college towns which he visited, an *event salesman* asked him what breed his new dog was. This made him extremely angry, and his shouting and screaming aroused the indignation of a *confirmed flat,* who ordered his immediate arrest. But being in with all the *blessed professor,* Mr. Ables was soon released.

2. THE KNAUGHUPELLAR

(Par: 5 min.)

WE PERMIT SMOKING
PLEASE DO NOT FEED OR
ANNOY THE ANIMALS.

X

THE KNAUGHUPELLAR

This animal is a Knaughupellar. He was first discovered in the Northern section of Kansas City and is now in a zoo in Quebec. Above this animal there is a sign which bears the X of the illiterate zoo keeper. Now, the trick is to fill in each square in the Knaughupellar with a letter taken from the sign in such a way as to spell the names of 11 animals, 1 small creeping animal and 1 insect. As you put each letter in each square in the Knaughupellar cross it out in the sign, and when you have finished, every letter in the sign will be crossed out and the Knaughupellar will be completely filled in. The 4 letters already placed in the squares will serve to guide you (they were not taken from the sign) and, as a further help, we will start you off with TIGER, the animal in the hind leg (reading from top to bottom). The G is already there so all you need to cross out in the sign are the letters T, I, E and R. Now, go ahead!

3. DESERVED

(Par: 5 min.)

Mr. I. M. Neverong gave me a check in full payment for some work which I had done for him. The check was in three figures and for much more than my bill, I was informed, so naturally I was very pleased. As a further gesture of his great generosity, Mr. Neverong told me that if I promised not to cash the check (which I hadn't seen as yet) he would give me the difference between the product of the three digits and their sum—and he assured me that this difference would not be a small number. Of course I jumped at this but when I saw the check I realized what a fool I was. How much was the check?

4. MR. AND MRS. G. WATT SUCKERS

(Par: 5 min.)

Mr. and Mrs. G. Watt Suckers met two strange men on a recent boat trip and started to play bridge with them. Just after the first hand was dealt Mr. G. Watt Suckers was called away. While he was gone one of the strangers started to play solitaire with the other pack of cards. He spread the cards on the table as shown below and then changed his mind and picked them up again. Mrs. G. Watt Suckers paid no attention to this apparently harmless action, but the other stranger was quite interested for it gave him a clue to his partner's hand.

Can you decipher the clue knowing that the suits represent vowels (a is spades, e hearts, i diamonds and o clubs) and the face value of the card represents the number of the letter in the alphabet (repeating after m viz: r is 1, s is 2, etc.) Each card, therefore, is a combination of a consonant and a vowel, with the exception of the cards that are face down. They represent two consonants. Tipped cards reverse the order (the vowel comes first instead of the consonant).

5. THE JORDAN ROBBERY

(Par: 6 min.)

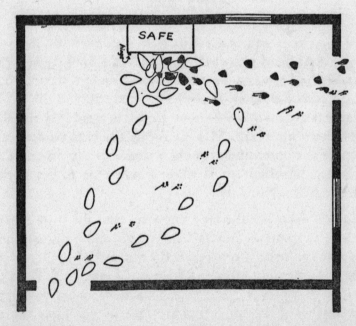

Kenneth Jordan's house was robbed a few weeks ago and the burglar was caught.

Here are the three stories which were told at police head-quarters. See if you can tell by studying the diagram, which story is true, why it must be true and just what happened.

Mr. Jordan said: I heard a noise in the other room. I got up, put on my slippers and when I saw the burglar bending over my safe, I called Fido, who ran after the thief. I then went to the safe and found that all my valuable papers were stolen.

The Burglar said: I entered the house but I didn't open the safe because the dog chased me before I had a chance to do it. I did not rob the safe.

The Detective said: It sounds fishy to me. I say Jordan robbed himself to get the insurance. He took the papers out of the safe after the thief had fled.

6. HALT AND GIVE THE COUNTERSIGN

(Par: 2 min.)

Several words have been omitted in the following paragraphs and numbers have been supplied in their places. These numbers are determined by their position in a 10-letter word, the letters of which are numbered in order 1234567890. For example, if the word were DUMBWAITER (which it isn't) then D would be 1, U would be 2, etc. How fast can you supply the missing words and find the key word?

If you have never 5220 43 70 90 97136902, you have a 1296 thrill in store for you. The other day I went from 372112 to 2172 70 0702 hours on a 345678 971 6702. It was one of the biggest thrills I ever had!

THE KEY WORD IS ....

7. PLEASE HELP LITTLE OTTO

(Par: 4 min.)

Little Otto was in the midst of his homework when his mother hit his father on the head with a shoe. Otto had to run out and get a doctor, and when he returned he was much too upset to give any thought to the multiplication problem which he had left undone. Help little Otto so that he won't get another F in arithmetic. *Just insert the correct number wherever there is a star in the example below.*

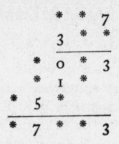

8. EDNA'S DILEMMA

(Par: 2 min.)

Edna said: "The man I marry will be tall, not fair, rather stout, foreign and will wear glasses and limp a trifle.

André is tall, dark, foreign and wears glasses but does not limp.

Perdo is not short, wears glasses and limps, is not dark and is by no means stout and is foreign.

David walks with a slight limp, is fair and not too stout, is not short and is certainly not dark. He wears glasses and is decidedly Russian.

Whom will Edna marry if these three men are her only chances?

9. THE HAPPY FAMILY

(Par: 1½ min.)

In the Brown family, each daughter has the same number of brothers as she has sisters, and each son has twice as many sisters as he has brothers.

How many sons and daughters are there in the Brown family?

10. THE LOGARITHMIC SPY

(Par: 10 min.)

During the last war, a suspicious-looking man was arrested in Paris and searched for secret messages. The search revealed a piece of a page torn from a book of logarithms. This paper appeared to be harmless and the authorities let him go. The next day, the French drive on a certain town was repulsed with considerable loss. Is this paper as innocent as it looks? Here is a reproduction of the paper:

Logs

N	0	1	2	3	4	5	6	7	8	9
5750	7596696	718	965	014	273	998	244	518	249	022
51	1265	715	814	313	055	620	426	719	820	971
52	4718	220	019	561	420	020	635	914		
53										

(Hint: The last figure or the last two figures of each log give the clue)

11. SALLY'S MOTHER

(Par: 2 min.)

Sally is just ⅛th as old as her mother. Sally's mother's age, when divided by 2, 3, 4, 6 and 8 always leaves one remaining year, but when divided by 5 there is nothing left over.

How old is Sally?

12. ARE YOU SUSCEPTIBLE TO CODES?

(Par: 4 min.)

Just before an important battle in the last war, an eccentric looking man was arrested in Paris. He gave his name as Ivan Popovitch and his vocation as a statistician. He said that he was on his way to Russia to gather information about the population of Russian cities. The following scrap of paper was found on him:

Menstirk 457,682
Mnudretlv 965,432
Mnydoaski 152,463
Mnzepotloff 74,251

He was promptly arrested as a German spy. Can you decode the message?

13. SOME GANG

(Par: 2 min.)

A party of 10 consists of 2 grandfathers, 2 grandmothers, 3 fathers, 3 mothers, 3 sons, 3 daughters, 2 mothers-in-law, 2 fathers-in-law, 1 son-in-law, 1 daughter-in-law, 2 brothers and 2 sisters. How is this possible?

14. WHO SAID SO?

(Par: 5 min.)

From what authors are the following quotations taken?

1. A thing of beauty is a joy forever.
2. One may smile and smile and be a villain.
3. Give me liberty or give me death.
4. He prayeth best who loveth best.
5. Hell is paved with good intentions.
6. Knowledge is power.
7. Thus Conscience does make cowards of us all.
8. The only reward of virtue is virtue.
9. "I doubt it," said the carpenter and shed a bitter tear.
10. His brow is wet with honest sweat.

15. ALONE IN A CROWD

(Par: 6 min.)

"Last night," said Julian, "I dined with my step-brother's nephew's father, my father's mother-in-law's husband and my step-mother's father-in-law, yet I dined alone!

Julian told the truth. How is this possible?

16. KST

(Par: 2 min.)

In a certain word of eight letters, KST is in the middle, in the beginning and at the end. There is only one K, one S and one T in the word.

What is the word?

17. THE PLOT THICKENS

(Par: 4 min.)

How quickly can you divide up this plot of ground into sixteen smaller plots, each of equal size and all of the same shape as the diagram shown below?

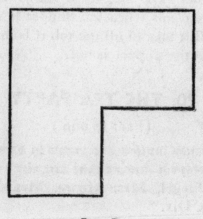

18. CAPITAL STUFF

(Par: 3 min.)

Mr. Franklin and Mr. Smith have exactly the same amount of money. Mr. Franklin, however, is richer than Mr. Dobbs, and Mr. Dobbs is richer than Mr. Hill. Mr. Brewster, who is poorer than Mr. Franklin, but richer than Mr. Hill, is not as rich as Mr. Dobbs. Mr. Smith is poorer than Mr. Dick.

Is Mr. Hill richer or poorer than Mr. Smith?
Is Mr. Brewster richer or poorer than Mr. Franklin?
Is Mr. Dick richer or poorer than Mr. Dobbs?
Is Mr. Franklin richer or poorer than Mr. Hill?
Is Mr. Dobbs richer or poorer than Mr. Brewster?
Who is the richest?
Who is the poorest?

If, by rich or poor is always meant the fixed sum of $1250, and if the poorest man has only $5 to his name, how much has each man?

19. TROUBLE IN THE BATH ROOM

(Par: 4 min.)

The cold water tap in a bath tub can fill the tub with water in 6 minutes and 40 seconds. The hot tap can fill this tub in exactly eight minutes. The tub, when filled, will empty in 13 minutes and 20 seconds when the stopper is removed.

How long will it take to fill the tub if both faucets are going full blast and the stopper is out?

20. THE TEA PARTY

(Par: 10 min.)

A woman recently invited five guests to a tea. The names of the six women who sat down to the circular table were: Mrs. Mendes, Mrs. Siegel, Mrs. Moore, Mrs. Newman, Mrs. Jacobs, and Mrs. Dix.

One of these women was deaf, one was very fat, one was quite talkative, one was a bromidic soul, one simply hated Mrs. Dix, and one was the hostess.

The woman who hated Mrs. Dix sat directly opposite Mrs. Jacobs. The deaf woman sat opposite Mrs. Siegel, who sat between the bromidic soul and the woman who hated Mrs. Dix. The fat woman sat opposite Mrs. Moore, next to the deaf woman and to the left of the woman who hated Mrs. Dix. The bromidic soul sat between Mrs. Siegel and the woman who sat opposite the woman who hated Mrs. Dix. Mrs. Mendes, who was a good friend of everyone—particularly Mrs. Dix—sat next to the fat woman and opposite the hostess.

Can you identify each of these charming women?

21. THE SHOPPERS

(Par: 5 min.)

Mrs. Adams, Mrs. Baker, Mrs. Catt, Mrs. Dodge, Mrs. Ennis and poor old Mrs. Fisk all went shopping one morning at The Emporium. Each woman went directly to the floor carrying the article which she wanted to buy, and each woman bought only one article. The following articles were bought: a book, a dress, a handbag, a necktie, a hat and a lamp.

All the women, except Mrs. Adams, entered the elevator on the ground floor. There were, also, two men in the elevator. Two women, Mrs. Catt and the one who bought the necktie, got off at the second floor. Dresses were sold on the third floor. The two men got off at the fourth floor. The woman who bought the lamp got off at the fifth floor, leaving poor old Mrs. Fisk all alone to get off at the sixth floor.

The next day Mrs. Baker, who received a handbag as a surprise gift from the woman who got off at the second floor, met Mr. Baker (her husband) returning the necktie one of the other women had given him. If books are sold on the main floor, and Mrs. Ennis was the sixth person to get out of the elevator, what did each of these women buy?

22. PUT THESE COLLEGE MEN IN THEIR PLACES

(Par: 5 min.)

Johnson, Barry, Brewster, Edwards, Adams and Hunter are each sophomores in one of the following colleges:

Yale, Harvard, Princeton, Dartmouth, Cornell and Columbia.

Miss Short is Barry's girl. Miss Philips is Brewster's girl. Miss Klag is Hunter's girl. Miss Rice is Johnson's girl. Miss West is Edwards' girl.

Miss Philips doesn't know any Cornell men.

Miss Klag never met any Columbia men.

Miss West hates Harvard men.

Miss Kent roots for Princeton.

Brewster knows Miss West but she won't have anything to do with him.

Barry wears a big Y on his sweater.

To which college does each man go?

23. DRAMATIS PERSONAE

(Par: 9)

We've rounded up fifteen of the better known people in some of the best known books. The attached list of books, however, has been woefully scrambled. It's up to you to revise this listing so that Joe Harper and John Ridd and the rest of them are returned to their natural setting.

1. Ben Gunn   Lorna Doone
2. Uriah Heep   Cyrano de Bergerac
3. Lucy Manette   The Count of Monte Cristo
4. Carol Kennicott   The Forsyte Saga
5. Catherine Barkley   Vanity Fair
6. Roxanne   A Tale of Two Cities
7. Joe Harper   Silas Marner

[48]

24. CRYPTOGRAM

By Franklin Watts

(Par: 30 min.)

The following well-known poem is written in cipher. The order of the words and punctuation has been left as in the original.

For those who have never worked a cryptogram a few hints may be in order. The most frequently recurring letter in the language is "e." The most common three-letter word is "the." The only single-letter words in common usage are "a" and "I."

O TAWAWPAT, O TAWAWPAT
RYA YECIA SYATA O SMI PETH,
RYA JORRJA SOHGES SYATA RYA ICH
FMWA DAADOHK OH MR WETH;
YA HANAT FMWA M SOHQ REE IEEH,
HET PTECKYR REE JEHK M GMX,
PCR HES, O EBRAH SOIY RYA HOKYR
YMG PETHA WX PTAMRY MSMX!

Score ½ point for each correct letter and 100 for a perfect score.

25. WHOZOO?

(Par: 8)

Indicate the profession or vocation of each of the people listed below, and which ones are dead, by writing the letter D after the profession or vocation.

1. Emil Coué
2. Howard Thurston
3. Charles Ponzi
4. Roald Amundsen
5. John S. Sumner
6. Howard Scott
7. Billy Sunday
8. Ring Lardner
9. Rudyard Kipling
10. "Daddy" Browning
11. Giulio Gatti-Casazza
12. James Joyce

26. THINK COW IT IS DONE

(Par: 2 min.)

A farmer died leaving his entire herd of cattle to his 5 sons on the following conditions:

Son John to get ⅓rd of the herd; Son Tom to get ¼th of the herd; Son Henry to get ⅙th of the herd; Son Bill to get ⅛th of the herd; Son George to get ⅑th of the herd.

Of course, the cattle could not be divided up the way the will specified, so a kind neighbor was called in to help out. The kind neighbor loaned two of his cows, and everything came out okay. Each son received his exact share of the cattle according to the will, and the kind neighbor took back his two cows after the division was over.

How many cows were there in the farmer's herd and what was each son's share?

What is wrong with the problem?

27. AS EASY AS ROLLING OFF A LOG

(Par: 10 min.)

Roland R. Rolling boasts that he is the second best log-roller west of Marshalltown, Iowa. The other day he complained that he was tired. He said that he had given an exhibition, in which he walked at a uniform rate from one end to the other, of 40 different logs, while the logs were rolling down a gentle incline.

As soon as the particular log he was on stopped rolling (at the bottom of the incline), he would get off and walk back to the top of the incline and start on the next log. He did this until the 40 logs were rolled from the top of the incline to the bottom.

If 25% of these logs were 30 inches in diameter and 10 feet long and rolled 20 yards, and the rest of the logs were 2 feet in diameter and 12 feet long and rolled 15 yards, how far has Roland R. Rolling walked, assuming that he finished where he started?

(*Hint: the total distance Rolling walks on any one log is the hypotenuse of a right triangle with the log as one arm and the distance rolled as the other.*)

28. THE LITERARY GANGSTER

(Par: 10 min.)

It isn't often you see a gangster quoting from Shakespeare, but here's one. He was caught after a round-up in Chicago, and the following quotation and letters were found in his pocket:

G E N T E H
K O J D I Y
A K Z Y P G
O A E X G R
E W S Q M N
W T N E I M

Round about the cauldron go
In the poison'd entrails throw.
Toad, that under cold stone
Days and nights has thirty-one. . . .

What does the message say? If you were a cop, where would you look for the gangsters?

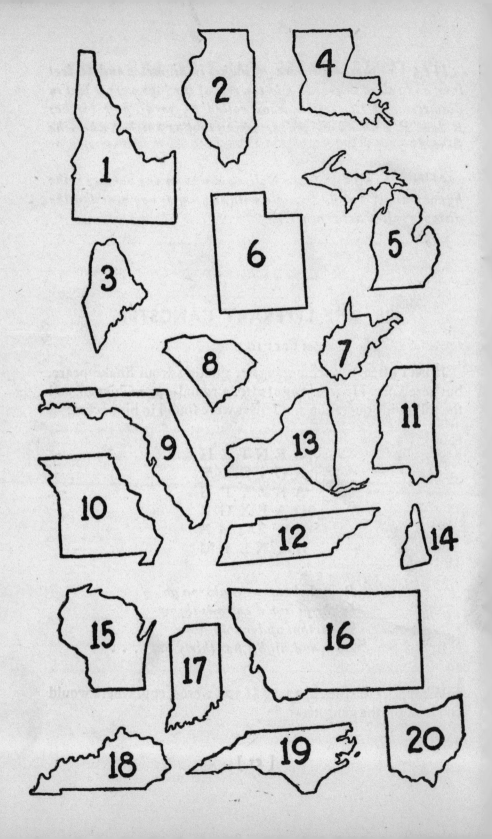

29. THESE STATES WANT TO BE NAMED

(Par: 15 min.)

Can you identify the states shown on the opposite page? They are all drawn to the same scale. See how many of them you know.

1. ....
2. ....
3. ....
4. ....
5. ....
6. ....
7. ....
8. ....
9. ....
10. ....
11. ....
12. ....
13. ....
14. ....
15. ....
16. ....
17. ....
18. ....
19. ....
20. ....

30. AN H OF A PROBLEM

(Par: 4 min.)

Here you have the letter "H," before and after being broken up into fragments. Can you put the pieces together again, without cutting them out, to reform the letter?

31. THE ROYAL TRIANGLE

(Par: 8 min.)

In the three cards shown below:

a. There's at least one Queen just to the right of a King.
b. There's at least one Queen just to the left of a Queen.
c. There's at least one Spade just to the left of a Heart.
d. There's at least one Spade just to the right of a Spade.

Name All Three Cards

Card No. 1. ....

Card No. 2. ....

Card No. 3. ....

32. UPSIDE TURVY POKER

(Par: 10 min.)

In a friendly little five-handed game, Player No. 3 said he held the only possible hand which would win; but he showed only the Four of Spades.

See how quickly you can name the four cards shown back up, remembering that the game is POKER.

The hand held by No. 3 is: (Check one)   a. A Straight. b. A Straight Flush.   c. Four-of-a-kind.   d. A Flush.   e. A Royal Flush.   f. A Full House.

33. LOONY HEADLINES

(Par: 5 min.)

A newspaper editor went blotto one day and wrote the three goofy sentences below, to be used as headlines for news items in the morning edition. Luckily they got into the hands of a rewrite man before they were printed, and he was able to transpose the words so they made good sense.

Can You Do the Same?

You must use every word, paying close attention to capital and small letters, possessives, and plurals. Your three new sentences must each have five words, just like the loony ones.

Here's how they looked when the editor first wrote them:

1. Japan's convicts will get Derby.
2. French horse wins Count's navy.
3. Three years equal twice nine.

Write the sentences correctly in the spaces below:

1. ....
2. ....
3. ....

Score: If all sentences are correct, count 100.

For each misplaced word in final answer, subtract 25.

34. PROBLEM IN JABBERWOCKY

(Par: 4 min.)

a. A DAKE is exactly four SMAGS in length.
b. A QUATTOL holds water; so does a TOLQUAT.
c. The top of a QUATTOL measures 1 SMAG by 1 SMAG.
d. The top of a TOLQUAT measures 1 DAKE by 1 DAKE.
e. A QUATTOL is one DAKE in depth.
f. A TOLQUAT is one SMAG in depth.

Question 1. If both the QUATTOL and the TOLQUAT are box-shaped with parallel sides, which one holds more water?

Question 2. How much more?

35. I WOULDN'T TRUST HER WITH MY MONEY!

(Par: 6 min.)

Mrs. G. I. Emma Sucker did some shopping recently in a very queer manner. She paid a dollar to enter shop A where she spent exactly one-half of what she had left, for a rubber saw. She then paid a dollar to get out of shop A and entered shop B where, paying a dollar to enter, she spent exactly one-half of what she had left, for a lame parrot. She then paid a dollar to get out of shop B and paid another dollar to enter shop C where she spent exactly one-half of what she had left, for artificial hair oil. She then paid a dollar to get out of shop C and, having very little cash left, decided to spend it all in Shop D. She accordingly paid a dollar to enter shop D, spent exactly half of what she had left for buttermilk, and paid her last dollar to get out. The foolish woman was then completely broke. How much did Mrs. Sucker have in cash before she entered shop A and how much did she spend for each of the four items mentioned?

36. THE ETERNAL WRECTANGLE

(Par: 10 min.)

Believe it or not, four men were married four times to the same four women so that each man in turn was married to the other man's wife.

"I was Phil Daniel's first wife" said Mrs. Lamson to Mrs. Prince.

"Ah, dear Phil," replied Mrs. Prince who was Mr. Colt's first wife, "I married him a week after he divorced you. Mrs. Colt was my husband's first wife. He divorced her and married the present Mrs. Daniels."

"Now you let the cat out of the bag," exclaimed Mrs. Lamson. "I always wanted to know whom my husband married before he married me. Now you have told me!"

Whom did Mr. Lamson marry before he married the present Mrs. Lamson and who was Mr. Colt's second wife?

(*Hint: make a diagram of 16 squares as follows and fill it in.*)

	C	D	L	P
1				
2				
3				
4	*c*	*d*	*ℓ*	*ρ*

37. PERSONAL PROPERTY

(Par : 6 min.)

"I just bought a piece of property in the shape of a square 600 feet on each side," said Sap.

"Good for you," said Yap. "What are you going to do with it?"

"I am going to fence off a triangular piece in the center, 300 feet on each side, and every month for 24 months I am going to increase the perimeter of this triangle by at least 300 feet," replied Sap.

"You can't do that," said Yap. "After the 4th month you will be way outside of your property limits."

At this point, Sap took out a pencil and paper to explain how he would do it, but a sudden gust of wind blew the paper away!

How would Sap accomplish this amazing feat?

38. FAMILY SKELETON

(Par: 10 min.)

How old is my grandfather and how old are my three children and I? (*See diagram on next page.*)

Horizontal

1. The year in which my grandfather was born.
3. The cube of my daughter's age next year.
6. The cube of my youngest child's age and the square of my daughter's present age. (2 digits)

7. Twice my grandfather's age when he died 20 years ago. (3 digits)

Vertical

1. The cube of my oldest son's age (he is 31 years younger than I am).
2. Grandfather's age last year.
4. My present age.
5. Nearly a century.
6. My grandfather's lucky number.
8. My grandfather's age when I was born.
9. The square root of my grandfather's birth year.

39. THE TRESTLE WALKERS

(Par: 6 min.) *See diagram on next page.*

These three young men started walking across a trestle at the beginning of it. The beginning of the trestle is not shown, but you can see the end of it. C is about to step off the trestle with his next stride. The lengths of the steps taken by A, B and C, respectively, differ from each other, but do not vary from themselves. The sleepers are evenly spaced.

WHAT IS THE SHORTEST POSSIBLE LENGTH OF THE TRESTLE AND HOW FAR HAS EACH OF THESE YOUNG MEN WALKED?

40. IT'S FUN TO BE FOLD

(Par: 9 min.)

A piece of ordinary typewriter paper (8½″ x 11″) is folded as shown below. Can you find the length of the fold?

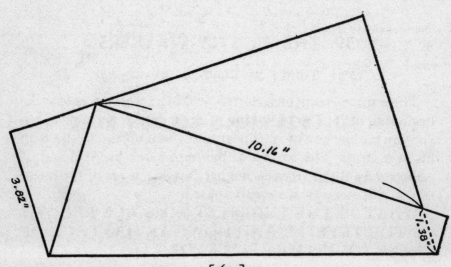

10.16″
3..82″
1.38″

41. HIGH FINANCE

(Par: 3 min.)

Ike gave Mike as many dollars as Mike already had. When Mike received this money, he asked Ike how much he had left, and promptly gave this amount back to Ike. Ike, not to be outdone by Mike's generosity, gave Mike back as many dollars as Mike had left, which left poor Ike dead broke and gave Mike $80 altogether. How much had each man in the beginning?

42. FULL NAME PLEASE

(Par: 6)

The following ten names are well known but the initials are not so well known. Can you fill in the names for which the initials stand?

1. H. G. Wells ....
2. G. B. Stern ....
3. G. K. Chesterton ....
4. H. L. Mencken ....
5. P. G. Wodehouse ....
6. P. T. Barnum ....
7. A. E. Housman ....
8. O. O. McIntyre ....
9. T. S. Eliot ....
10. J. P. Morgan ....

43. COLLEGE MEN'S GOLDEN RULE

(Par: 2 min.)

Here is a golden rule to go by. Can you read it?
2B CONTINUALLY
E co X n f A i d M e n S t
I d S i H m E S
llllllll chances T 4 H 6 E s M

44. A WEIGHTY PROBLEM

(Par: 10 min.)

An iron bar weighs 40 pounds. Into what 4 weights must I break this bar to enable me, with the aid of these 4 pieces, to weigh 1, 2, 3, 4, 5, etc. pounds all the way up to 40 pounds, on a balance. I may either add to or subtract from, but I must be able to produce all the weights from 1 pound to 40.

45. QUINTUPLETS ON THE SQUARE

(Par: 10 min.)

Can you transform this square into five small squares, all equal to one another, whose total area shall be equal to this square?

46. NOT SO EASY

(Par: 10 min.) *See diagram on next page.*

A square 8″ on each side is cut as shown—the shaded portion being the part which has been removed. Can you draw two lines in the remaining pentagon, dividing the figure into three parts which will fit together to form a perfect square? Can you prove that it is a square and tell what the length of each of its sides is?

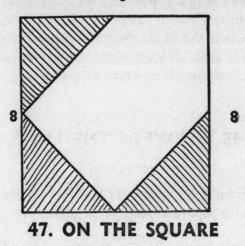

47. ON THE SQUARE

(Par: 30 min.)

Can you place the numbered circles, triangles and squares into the twelve blank spaces below so that no two similar figures and no two similar numbers appear in any horizontal or vertical row or in either diagonal? This, of course, includes the numbers already in the diagram.

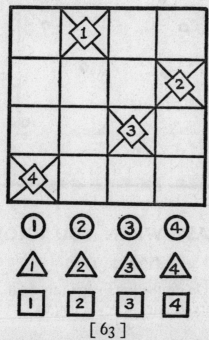

If you prefer doing this puzzle with playing cards, place the four aces as shown in the diagram, then arrange the kings, queens and jacks in the blank spaces so that no two cards of the same suit or the same denomination appear in any horizontal row or vertical column, or in either diagonal.

48. BETWEEN THE LINES

(Par: 15 min.)

In the diagram below draw six lines across the rectangle in such a way as to separate each small circle from every other small circle.

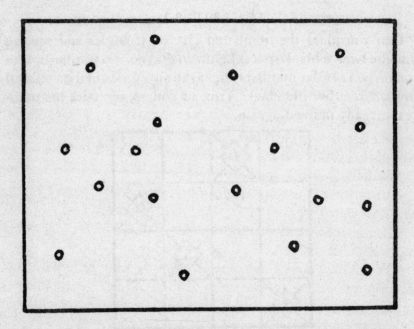

49. IT'S EASY WHEN YOU KNOW HOW

(Par: 20 min.)

Divide the circle on the next page into four equal parts by drawing three curved lines of equal length.

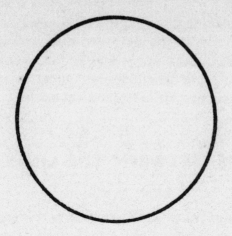

50. TOO MUCH IS ENOUGH

(Par: 20 min.)

"I divided $16.00 among my children yesterday," said Uncle Jack.

"Yes," said I. "How come?"

"Well, you see it was this way: no one got less than $4.00 and two of them received the same amount."

"So what," said I, looking bored.

"Just in case you want to figure out how many children I have and how much I gave to each one," he replied.

"But how can I on that flimsy information?" I said, growing more impatient.

"Well, I suppose I ought to tell you that the product of the various amounts I gave to each of them equals the number of square inches in a certain number of square feet. That's enough information, isn't it?"

Can you figure out how many children Uncle Jack has and how much money he gave to each one of them?

Part III

TEST YOURSELF

HOW GOOD A WITNESS ARE YOU?

To Test Your Powers of Observation

The following pages are designed to enable you to see what sort of witness you would make. In each of the three pictures shown something is happening and it is up to you to describe the scene as accurately as you can by answering as many of the twenty-five questions as you are able to answer. The following rating will serve as a guide:

20 to 25 correct answers	EXCELLENT
15 to 20 correct answers	GOOD
10 to 15 correct answers	AVERAGE
5 to 10 correct answers	POOR
0 to 5 correct answers	VERY POOR

THE HIBERGH ACCIDENT

If you were present for three minutes at the scene of this accident how much could you tell about it on the witness stand? Study this picture carefully for three minutes noting everything in it, then, without referring to the picture again, see how many of the questions on the other side of this page you can answer.

1. At what time did the accident happen? ....

2. What was the date? ....

3. At the intersection of what two streets did it happen? ....

4. Who was struck, a man or a woman? ....

5. Was this person knocked down? ....

6. Who owns the truck? ....

7. What is the owner's address? ....

8. What is the owner's telephone number? ....

9. What does the company deal in? ....

10. What is the number of the truck? ....

11. Is the truck going toward the company's office? ....

12. How many people saw the accident? ....

13. What are they doing about it? ....

14. Did the driver see the accident? ....

15. What store is on the corner? ....

16. Who owns it? ....

17. What is its number? ....

18. What is the address of L. H. Metz? ....

19. What does he sell? ....

20. What store is to the right of Metz? ....

21. Who owns it? ....

22. What direction is the truck going? ....

23. Where is the hydrant? ....

24. Is there a letter box in the picture? ....

25. Where is the fire alarm? ....

THE FLOTOWN FIRE

If you stood looking at this scene for three minutes how well could you describe it to a friend who had not seen it? Study this picture carefully for three minutes noting everything in it, then, without referring to the picture again, see how many of the questions on the next page you can answer.

1. In what building is the fire? ....
2. On what floor is it? ....
3. Are there any flames or did you just see smoke? ....
4. What time is shown in the picture? ....
5. What is the date? ....
6. What is the address of the burning building? ....
7. What is the name of the building next door to it? ....
8. What is the address of this building? ....
9. Is there a fire alarm shown? ....
10. How many people saw the fire? ....
11. What are they doing about it? ....
12. Where is the drug store? ....
13. Who owns it? ....
14. What store is next to the drug store? ....
15. Who owns it? ....
16. What two stores are in the hotel? ....
17. Who owns which? ....
18. Did you notice any fire escapes on the burning building? ....
19. Where are the fire escapes? ....
20. How many floors are there in the burning building? ....
21. How many floors are there in the hotel? ....
22. Are there any car tracks shown? ....
23. What is the name of the park? ....
24. Did you notice any traffic? ....
25. Where is the fire hydrant? ....

THE POMPTON HOLDUP

Suppose you saw this holdup and then ran over to police headquarters to report it. How accurately could you do it? Study this picture carefully for three minutes then, without referring to it again answer as many questions as you can on the next page.

1. What was held up? ....
2. What is the address? ....
3. How much did the thief take? ....
4. What is the thief doing? ....
5. What is the name of the taxi? ....
6. What is the number of the taxi? ....
7. On what street is the taxi? ....
8. Which direction is the taxi going? ....
9. What time did the holdup take place? ....
10. What is the date? ....
11. What is the cop doing? ....
12. How many people saw the holdup? ....
13. How many people are shown in the picture? ....
14. Who owns the corner store? ....
15. What does he sell? ....
16. In front of which store is the tree? ....
17. Who owns it? ....
18. Is the taxi on the wrong side of the street? ....
19. On what street is the real estate place? ....
20. What is address of the cigar store? ....
21. On which street are the car tracks? ....
22. Which street is the one way street? ....
23. In front of which store is the clock? ....
24. Where is the hydrant? ....
25. Did you notice any steep hill? ....

HOW GOOD A DETECTIVE ARE YOU?

To Test Your Powers of Deduction

The following five picture clues are designed by Lawrence Treat to test your powers of deduction and your detective ability. The pictures are all drawn with extreme care and contain all the information necessary to solve the crimes which they represent. Read the directions carefully then read the story connected with each of the pictures. After you have done so try to solve the crime by answering the questions and giving logical reasons for your answers.

If you find this too difficult you may refer to the method of approach which the author has given.

Ratings

Without referring to the method of approach:

        80 to 100% correct   EXCELLENT
        60 to 80% correct   VERY GOOD
        40 to 60% correct   GOOD
        20 to 40% correct   FAIR
         0 to 20% correct   POOR

Referring to the method of approach:

        80 to 100%   VERY GOOD
        60 to 80%   GOOD
        40 to 60%   FAIR
        20 to 40%   POOR

Under 20%   DON'T TRY TO BE A DETECTIVE!

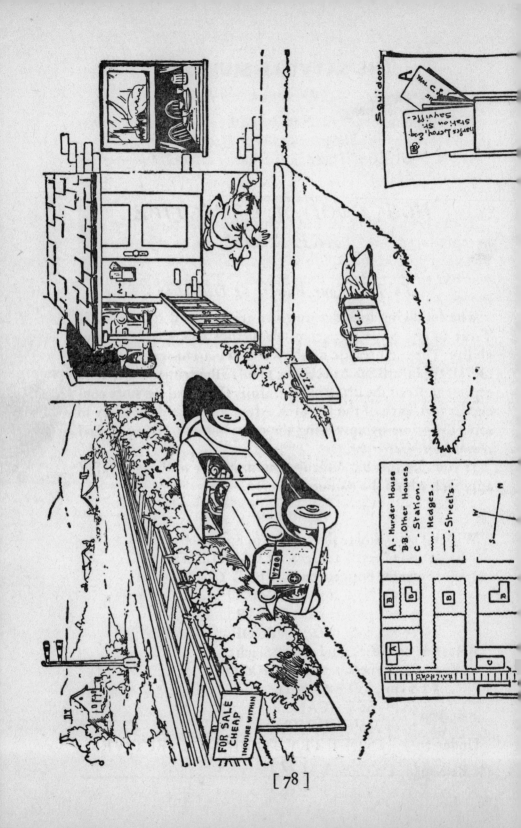

THE SAYVILLE MURDER

Directions

Read the statement first. Next study the picture. Then answer the questions by checking the box next to the correct answer.

DON'T GUESS. There is a definite, logical clue to every answer.

Statement

If you heard a shot, rushed to this house and found it exactly as reproduced, with the murdered man lying on the porch and breakfast still on the table and partly eaten, could you deduce who had committed the crime and why? The sketch reproduces the scene of a fatal shooting a few minutes after its occurrence, about nine o'clock one morning.

Questions—Check the Squares and Give Reason:

1. Is Charles Leroy apparently the occupant of the house?

Yes ☐
No ☐

Reason ....

2. Is he married?   Yes ☐
No ☐

Reason ....

3. Do you think the two pieces of baggage belonged to him?

Yes ☐
No ☐

Reason ....

4. What was his occupation?

Doctor ☐ Auto dealer ☐
Railroad man ☐
Travelling Salesman ☐

Reason ....

5. What was the occupation of the murdered man? Doctor ☐
Railroad man ☐ Auto dealer ☐ Travelling salesman ☐

Reason ....

6. To whom did the roadster in the driveway belong?

Leroy ☐ Murdered man ☐

Reason ....

7. Did the murdered man live here?   Yes ☐
                                      No ☐

Reason ....

8. How long do you think the roadster had been parked?
        All night ☐ A few minutes ☐
Reason ....

9. Had Leroy just left the house?   Yes ☐
                                     No ☐

Reason ....

10. Who had started breakfast with Mrs. Leroy?
        Leroy ☐ Murdered man ☐
Reason ....

11. Had the doctor made a professional call?   Yes ☐
                                                No ☐

Reason ....

12. Did Leroy drop his bags suddenly?   Yes ☐
                                         No ☐

Reason ....

13. What was the motive of the crime?
        Jealousy ☐ Robbery ☐
Reason ....

14. Do you think Leroy was guilty of the shooting?
                                        Yes ☐
                                        No ☐

Reason ....

Method of Approach (*A hint to the solution*).

*In reconstructing the crime, the following clues will be
helpful:*
The mail shows how many people lived here and who they
were. The stethoscope, which the murdered man always carried, shows his occupation. Look for evidence of whether he
lived here. The insignia on the radiator of the car shows to
whom it belonged, and the drip and the place where the car
was parked show whether it had been here for only a few minutes or for the entire night. The initials on the bag and sample
case show to whom they belonged and what his occupation was.

[80]

Now note where the coat was dropped and decide how a man ordinarily carries his coat when he has a bag in his hand; this will prove whether the man with the bags was leaving the house or returning to it. The map shows whether two people breakfasting at the window would feel safe from the observation of a neighbor or a chance passer-by. The proximity of the two chairs shows whether the two people who had been seated there were on unusually intimate terms. The bag in the car indicates whether its owner's visit was a professional one. Now return to the two bags and the coat; they show whether the person carrying them dropped them suddenly. Decide what he may have seen in the window, whether there was anything in sight that may have aroused his jealousy.

You now have the main facts in the case. Put them together and you can deduce who committed the murder and why.

THE HENDRICKS MURDER

Directions

Read the statement first. Everything in it is fact. Then study the picture. Finally answer the questions in order, inserting your reasons after the word *because*.

DON'T GUESS! There is a logical clue to every answer.

Statement

Hot tempered Hosiah Hendricks was shot on Thursday afternoon and discovered that evening as shown. His own revolver, kept in the rear of drawer A, was found outside the office with two discharged chambers. The death bullet pierced his skull and lodged in the wall.

Two men were questioned: His secretary, who went home at four and did not return, and his estranged son, Henry, who reached town at five and left again at seven.

The clock was running accurately until it was stopped, and Hendricks had not left his office since lunchtime.

Hendricks' office is just off the main line of a busy railroad.

On the basis of these facts and the evidence in the room, can you convict one of the two suspects of the murder of Hendricks? Check each box and give reasons.

1. Had Hendricks been working on Thursday afternoon?

    Yes ☐ No ☐

    Because ....

2. Was the safe blown open?

    Yes ☐ No ☐

    Because ....

3. May robbery have been the motive for the crime?

    Yes ☐ No ☐

    Because ....

4. Was Hendricks a poor man?

    Yes ☐ No ☐

    Because ....

5. Is Henry's departure on the 7 o'clock train conclusive proof of his guilt?

Yes ☐ No ☐

Because ....

6. Is it likely that the murderer obtained the gun while Hendricks was seated at his desk?

Yes ☐ No ☐

Because ....

7. Although people were within hearing distance all afternoon, no shots were heard. State a clue offering a reasonable explanation of this.

....

8. What was Hendricks doing at the moment he was shot?

He was ....

Because ....

9. Is there evidence of a fight?

Yes ☐ No ☐

Because ....

10. Where did the murderer stand when he shot Hendricks?

He stood near the window, ☐

He stood in front of the desk, ☐

He stood at the back of the desk, ☐

He stood near the front right corner of the desk, ☐

He stood at the point from which the sketch was made, ☐

He stood behind Hendricks, ☐

Because ....

11. Which shot struck the clock?

The first ☐ The second ☐

Because ....

12. Was Hendricks probably killed at six o'clock?

Yes ☐ No ☐

Because ....

13. Who killed Hendricks, and how?

The secretary ☐
Henry Hendricks ☐

as can be proved by the following three facts: 1. ....

.... ; 2. .... ;

3. ....

Method of Approach

In reconstructing the crime, the following clues will be helpful:

The safe indicates whether robbery was a possible motive. The position and attitude of the body show what Hendricks was doing at the time of his death and whether he received any warning of his impending fate. The curved railroad tracks and busy railroad show why no shot was heard. The position of drawer A shows whether the gun could have been taken without arousing Hendricks' apprehension. An imaginary line running from the bullet mark on the wall and through the head wound shows where the murderer must have stood; keeping his position in mind, decide whether the clock was in the line of fire. If so, was it struck accidentally and does it fix the time of the murder? If not, was it struck deliberately and does it fake the time of the murder? For what purpose may it have been intentionally shattered?

Restate the important evidence you have learnt thus far. It will enable you to decide who killed Hendricks, and to convict the murderer.

e 8, 1934 -

ng -

sband is back! He came late

i direct from the Pennsyl-

as terribly upset and jeal-

ip he'd heard. Luckily

ur name, but he found

tre ticket from yester-

ich you wrote your hotel

vening bag, and he took

and kill the man I

, Sam, he's dangerous

mise to go away at

o my sister —

115 Wyckoff Place

rried to death. I'm

nd - the butler's delivering

n't find you.

ur,

Lovey

B 113

$3.30

DTOWN THEATRE

EVENING 7
E

3-5000

END OF A WEALTHY PLAYBOY

On the opposite page, you will find two bits of paper that were clutched tightly in the lifeless hand of Gamut Ordway, as if guarded with his last breath.

Mr. Ordway's body, pierced by two bullets, was discovered in a New York hotel suite, which he had rented for a few days and for reasons unknown.

From these facts and from a study of the torn pieces, can you answer the questions and discover Ordway's murderer?

Answer the following questions by checking the box next to the correct answer, or by filling in the answer, as required. The first two questions have been done and explained for you, to show the type of reason you should have in mind.

1. Was the letter written to Ordway?

   Yes ☑ No ☐

   Because he is addressed as "Gam" (line 12).

2. Was Lovey's husband in town?

   Yes ☑ No ☐

   Because she begins by stating "sband (husband) is back" (line 3), and the tone of the letter shows she refers to her own husband.

Now you answer the rest of the questions.

3. Do you think Lovey's husband was jealous?

   Yes ☐ No ☐

   Because ....

4. In what month was the letter written? ....

   Because ....

5. How did Lovey's husband return?
   By car ☐ By train ☐ By plane ☐

   Because ....

6. What are the figures on the back of the ticket? An address ☐ A hotel room number ☐ A hotel phone number ☐ A private phone number ☐

   Because ....

[87]

7. Is it the same ticket as the one referred to in the letter?

Yes ☐ No ☐

Because ....

8. Do you think Ordway would be in danger if he met Lovey's husband?

Yes ☐ No ☐

Because ....

9. Did Lovey live at 115 Wyckoff Place?

Yes ☐ No ☐

Because ....

10. Was the letter mailed to Ordway?

Yes ☐ No ☐

Because ....

11. Write the complete word, part of which appears at the beginning of line 4. ....

12. Write the complete word, part of which appears at the beginning of line 6. ....

13. Write the complete word, part of which appears at the beginning of line 13. ....

14. Write the complete word, part of which appears at the beginning of line 16. ....

15. What was the motive of Ordway's murderer?

Theft ☐ Jealousy ☐ Insanity ☐

Because ....

16. How certain are you that Lovey's husband was the murderer?

I find the tone of the letter makes it very likely.

I find direct, convincing evidence.

Because ....

17. Have you any material from which you could trace the murderer, whose name you do not know?

Yes ☐ No ☐

Because ....

MERRILL'S ALIBI

On the next page you will find a picture of Merrill's room in Denver. The room, which shows all lights, appears exactly as it did at 7:40 p. m. one November evening, shortly before Merrill's arrest for the murder of D. B. Allen.

At 7 p. m. someone had shot Allen with a rifle and escaped by outrunning the watchman and scaling a high wall. Merrill's affair with Mrs. Allen provided him with a possible motive. In his car he could have reached the Allen estate in a half hour. The murderer was seen, and he resembled Merrill closely. If Merrill could give a satisfactory alibi, he could prove himself innocent. If not, the evidence was certain to convict him of the murder.

Mrs. Allen, in tears, said, "We were reading poetry at his apartment all afternoon. He didn't go out until a quarter of seven, when he bought a paper and a bulb and put me in a taxi."

Merrill said, "I went out only twice this evening—at six to buy a paper, at seven-thirty to buy a bulb, since mine had broken this afternoon. At seven I was home reading, right where my book still is."

From these facts and an examination of the room, can you answer the questions and decide whose story is true? If you believe neither Mrs. Allen nor Merrill, you send Merrill to the lethal chamber.

Answer the following questions by checking the box next to the correct answer. The first two questions have been done and explained for you, to show the type of reason you should have in mind.

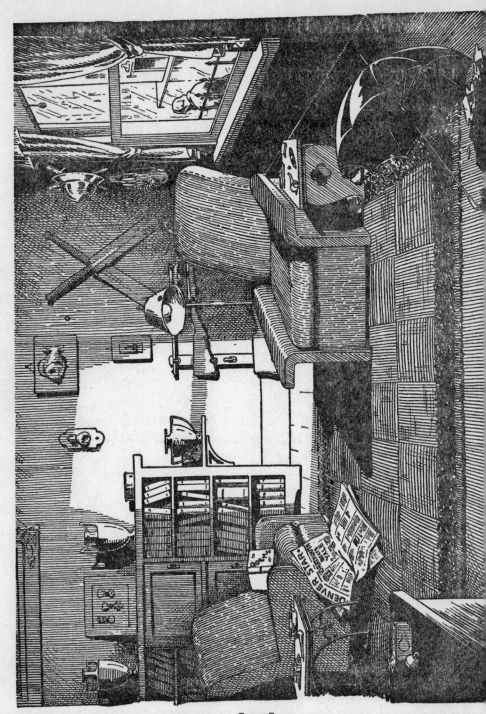

1. Did Merrill smoke? Yes ☑ No ☐
Because cigars, cigarettes, and particularly, a pipe may be seen.

2. Had it been raining recently? Yes ☑ No ☐
Because the umbrella is wet.

Now you answer the rest of the questions.

3. Do you think he was an athlete? Yes ☐ No ☐
Because ....

4. Is it likely that he could have outrun the watchman?
Yes ☐ No ☐
Because ....

5. Is it probable that he could have scaled a high wall?
Yes ☐ No ☐
Because ....

6. Is it likely that he was a good marksman? Yes ☐ No ☐
Because ....

7. Is the fact that none of the guns in the rack had been fired recently evidence of Merrill's innocence? Yes ☐ No ☐
Because ....

8. If Mrs. Allen's story is completely true, does it clear him?
Yes ☐ No ☐
Because ....

9. Do you think Merrill and Mrs. Allen had previously agreed on their stories? Yes ☐ No ☐
Because ....

10. Do you think she was in his apartment that day? Yes ☐
No ☐
Because ....

11. Can you prove that any part of her story was false? Yes ☐
No ☐
Because ....

12. Had Merrill apparently been reading his newspaper?
Yes ☑ No ☐
Because ....

13. On what floor was Merrill's apartment? Ground floor ☐
Second floor ☐ Above the second floor ☐
Because ....

14. The elevator boy did not know at what time Merrill went out. Is this fact evidence that Merrill sneaked out? Yes ☐ No ☐

    Because ....

15. How recently do you think Merrill was out? At 6:00 p. m. ☐ At 6:45 p. m. ☐ At 7:30 p. m. ☐

    Because ....

16. Merrill's alibi consisted of the facts stated below. Check the one or ones that you can prove false. I went out twice ☐ At six to buy a paper ☐ At seven-thirty to buy a bulb ☐ My bulb broke this afternoon ☐ At seven I was home ☐ At seven I was reading where my book is ☐

    Because ....

17. Have you saved Merrill from conviction? Yes ☐ No ☐

    Because ....

THE LUNCH ROOM MURDER

On the next page, you will find a sketch of Joe's lunch room. Police heard a shot, rushed to the restaurant, and found exactly what you see.

They identified the body as that of Flash Brady, a racketeer. Joe, who had no helper, had only one fact to tell. The murderer had leaned against the wall while firing at point blank range. The imprint of his gloved hand is in clear view.

From these facts and an examination of the scene, can you answer the questions and tell who killed Brady?

Answer the following questions by checking the box next to the correct answer. The first two questions have been done and explained to show the type of reason you should have in mind.

1. Had Joe been mopping up recently? Yes ☑ No ☐
   Because the pail, mop, and wet floor so indicate.
2. How many customers had recently been in the restaurant?
   None ☐ One ☐ Two ☐ Three ☐ Four ☑ Five ☐
   Because there are four checks and four plates, cups, glasses, and sets of cutlery.

Now you answer the rest of the questions.

3. Do you think Joe was the victim of a holdup? Yes ☐ No ☐
   Because ....
4. Do you think B, C and D knew each other? Yes ☐ No ☐
   Because ....
5. Did A enter the restaurant before D? Yes ☐ No ☐
   Because ....
6. At least how many people were in the restaurant the instant that Brady entered? 1 ☐ 2 ☐ 3 ☐ 4 ☐ 5 ☐ 6 ☐
   Because ....
7. Could Brady be seen approaching the restaurant by any of the customers? Yes ☐ No ☐
   Because ....
8. Would footsteps show if they had not traversed the wet spaces? Yes ☐ No ☐
   Because ....

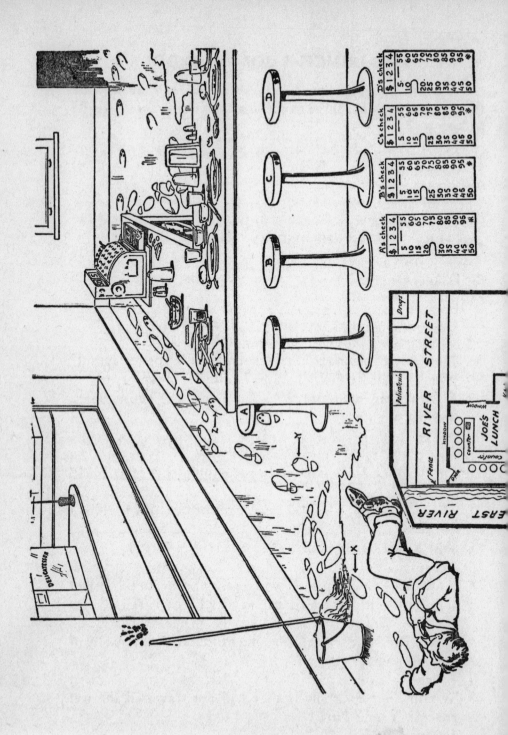

9. Which are Joe's footsteps? X □ Y □ Z □

Because ....

10. Did Joe walk out through the kitchen door? Yes □ No □

Because ....

11. Did Joe ring up the 55 cent sale on the cash register before the murder? Yes □ No □

Because ....

12. Where was Joe at the moment of the shooting? Near the mop □ Near the cash register □ Near the kitchen □

Because ....

13. Which are A's footsteps? X □ Y □ Z □

Because ....

14. Did A run out through the kitchen door? Yes □ No □

Because ....

15. Did B, C, and D leave through the front door? Yes □ No □

Because ....

16. Are the footsteps marked X those of the murderer? Yes □ No □

Because ....

17. Did the murderer fire with his right hand? Yes □ No □

Because ....

18. Who killed Brady? A □ B □ C □ D □ Joe □

Because ....

HOW GOOD IS YOUR MEMORY?

To Test Your Retentive Powers

Here are three good memory tests. Two are somewhat similar to the game we all used to play as children where a tray full of objects was shown to us and we were supposed to name every article on that tray when it was removed from view. These two tests are a little different because they show 26 objects, each object beginning with a different letter of the alphabet. There is for example an *A*corn, a *B*all, a *C*andle etc., all the way thru the alphabet and it is up to you to find each object in its proper alphabetical order and remember it so that when you turn the page you will be able to write its name after its initial letter and so fill in the 26 blanks. Remember that there is one and only one letter to each object. The eye glasses, for example cannot be called *s*pectacles because there is a *S*trainer shown. Therefore they must be *E*ye glasses. The third test is for number memory. If you can remember numbers of more than 8 digits your memory is excellent.

Rating:

22 to 26 objects correct	PHENOMENAL
18 to 22 " "	EXCELLENT
14 to 18 " "	VERY GOOD
10 to 14 " "	GOOD
6 to 10 " "	FAIR
Under 6 " "	POOR

MEMORY TEST NO. 1

Starting with Acorn find each object in its alphabetical order and try to remember as many of these as you can. After you have done this turn the page and fill these objects in under their correct initials. The animal shown in the lower left hand corner is a Yak.

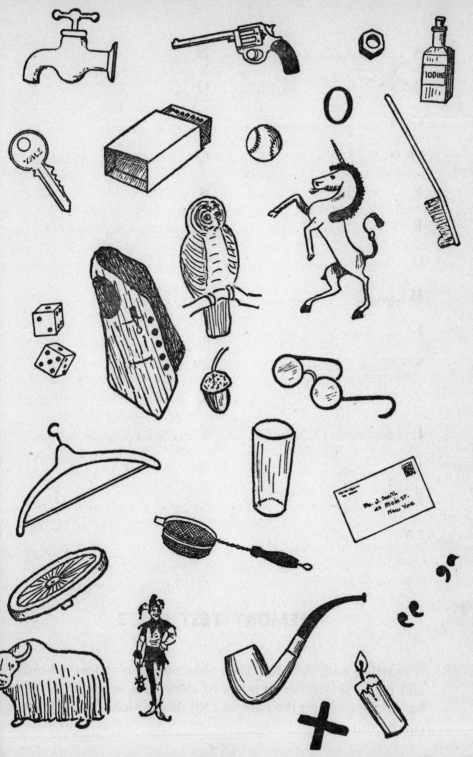

A ....   N ....

B ....   O ....

C ....   P ....

D ....   Q ....

E ....   R ....

F ....   S ....

G ....   T ....

H ....   U ....

I ....   V ....

J ....   W ....

K ....   X ....

L ....   Y ....

M ....   Z ....

MEMORY TEST NO. 2

Starting with Axe find each object in its alphabetical order and try to remember as many of these as you can. After you have done this turn the page and fill these objects in under their correct initials.

A	....	N	....
B	....	O	....
C	....	P	....
D	....	Q	....
E	....	R	....
F	....	S	....
G	....	T	....
H	....	U	....
I	....	V	....
J	....	W	....
K	....	X	....
L	....	Y	....
M	....	Z	....

NUMBER MEMORY TEST

Here is a real test for number memory. Place a piece of opaque paper over these numbers and then, starting with A, uncover it, look at it for a few seconds, cover it up again and write the number on the paper. Do the same for B and C, etc. See how far you can go without making a mistake. If you can get as far as L you are a wonder.

A	12792	I	65478390261
B	16485	J	75568103780
C	974865	K	52873510479
D	8467625	L	655374012967
E	45873602	M	748331029785
F	64783504	N	53662498013881
G	1736914092	O	43992710993645
H	6741936028	P	563429784013514

HOW GOOD IS YOUR IMAGINATION?

To Test Your Mechanical Sense

The following two diagrams are designed to test your imagination and also your sense of mechanics. Both pictures show systems of wheels, pulleys and levers. Sometimes the wheels are belted together, and sometimes they are in direct contact with one another. The ropes always have weights at both ends, and it is a simple matter to trace a rope from one end to the other. Knowing that wheels belted to one another revolve in the same direction unless the belt is crossed (in which case they revolve in opposite directions), that wheels in contact with one another revolve in opposite directions, and that if a weight goes down at one end of the rope the weight at the other end must go up, it is up to you to use your imagination in doing these problems.

AX ME ANOTHER

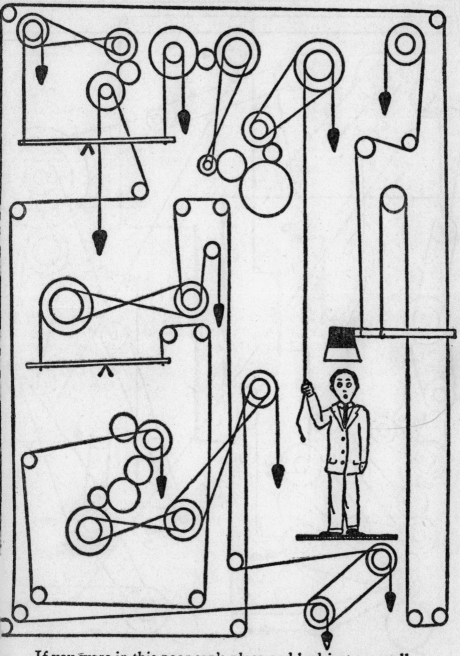

If you were in this poor sap's place and had just one pull or release of the rope what would you do—pull it or release it?

WHICH WAY PLEASE?

When a man steps on the treadle at A, how will all the weights move? Indicate this by arrows next to the weights.

HOW GOOD A DISTRICT ATTORNEY ARE YOU?

To Test Your Powers of Logic

We present, in this section, a number of logical problems which can be solved only by common sense and the process of elimination. Each of these problems will take at least 15 minutes to do, but you will find them all intensely interesting, simply because there is only one solution and it is up to you to find that solution, solely on the facts given and your own common sense.

THE FATAL ARGUMENT

In a deserted part of Brooklyn, about 3.30 A. M. on the night of January 14, four men got into a serious argument which resulted in one man killing one of the others. They all ran away after the fatal shot and were finally caught by the police and brought into headquarters. Unfortunately an innocent man, not in the crowd, got drawn in with them. Knowing the following facts, how quickly can you tell definitely who the murderer was, who the victim was, and who the innocent man was?

Tom—who had just met the murdered man and knew he controlled a gang, wouldn't dare to tell on the murderer.

Dick—who hates the murderer whom he has known for four years, is a pal of Fred's and a cousin of the murdered man.

Harry—who stood behind the murderer when he fired the fatal shot, was sure Tom did it.

Jack—who was in Philadelphia with his girl the evening of the murder and hasn't seen Dick for two years, was arrested in the Bronx two days later.

Fred—the boss of a powerful gang and an escaped convict, was the first man caught by the police.

THE HOLD-UP

(Par: 12 min.)

The First National Bank of Harrison, N. J., was held up on May 12th.

Four men were involved in the hold-up:

Rogers, Slim, Curley and The Rat. They were all taken to Police Headquarters and questioned. Each man made four simple statements, *only one of which is false.* See if you can find from their statements who was the guilty man.

1. Rogers said: I never was in Harrison. I did not hold up the bank. I know nothing of the robbery. The Rat and I were in Pittsburgh on May 12th.

2. Curley said: I am innocent. I was out with the Rat on May 12th. I never saw Rogers in my life. Rogers is innocent.

3. Slim said: Curley did it. Rogers and the Rat were never in Pittsburgh. I am innocent. Rogers helped Curley hold up the bank.

4. The Rat said: I did not hold up the bank. I was in Pittsburgh with Rogers on May 12th. I never saw Slim before. Slim lied when he said Rogers helped Curley do it.

WHO KILLED SULLIVAN?

Tim Sullivan, the keeper of a small restaurant in Hoboken, was shot and killed by a racketeer gang because he refused to pay for protection. After a great deal of rounding up, on the part of the police, five men were brought before the District Attorney who asked them what they had to say for themselves. Knowing that each man made three statements, only one of which is a lie, the brilliant District Attorney, by means of pure logic, arrested the murderer and it was not long before an indictment was brought against him. Can you do as well?

The members of the gang which were rounded up by the police are: Lefty, Red, Dago Tony, The Rat, and Skinny. Here is what each had to say (remember only one statement is false in each case):

Lefty: I did not kill Sullivan. I never killed anyone. The Rat did it.

Red: I did not kill Sullivan. I never owned a revolver. The other guys are all passing the buck.

Dago Tony: I know nothing of the murder. I never saw Skinny before. The Rat is guilty.

The Rat: I am innocent. Skinny is the guilty man. Lefty lied when he said I did it.

Skinny: I know nothing of the murder. Red is the guilty man. Tony will vouch for me—he's known me for years.

[108]

HOW GOOD IS YOUR TIME SENSE?

To Test Your Ability to Think in an Orderly Way

The following five time puzzles were created and illustrated by Gerald Lynton Kaufman, author of *IT'S ABOUT TIME* and member of the Society of American Magicians.

Remember that Time is what makes things take place. It is like a one way street and there is no going back! There is only one possible order in which things can happen and it is up to you to find that order in these Time Pictures which are all mixed up. You must rearrange these pictures in their logical Time order and number them correctly. Then you must tell what happened. They are lots of fun to do!

TIME TO CHEER UP

While the four merry makers were enjoying their late supper party, Leonardo Hawkeye, the artist sleuth, made these eight sketches of the evidence. Only he forgot to number them in order. Can you do it?

The celebration was at the home of Bill and Mary Stuyvesant-Smith, and took place after they returned from the theatre with their friends George and Dorothy, who had just become engaged. The four of them came in at 11:30 P.M., and the party didn't break up until 2:00 A.M.

The pitcher contains lemonade—perhaps with some gin in it. One plate contains olives. The other plate contains bridge-cookies. The cake is a rich chocolate cake, baked by Mary that afternoon.

THE PROBLEM:—*First number the pictures in order. Then answer these questions, and see how accurately you can find the evidence.*

By the way, it is important to know that everyone was very polite when the party began.

1. What did Dorothy take for her first drink?
2. Who took the second glass and what was in it?
3. Who took the third glass and what was in it?
4. Between which pictures did the second round of drinks occur?
5. Did some of the people mix their drinks?
6. Did everybody probably take cake?
7. Can you find three reasons to prove that someone came to the table between Nos. 1 and 2?
8. Is there evidence that someone came to the table between Nos. 2 and 3?
9. Can you find five ways to prove No. 2 later than No. 1?
10. Can you find four ways to prove No. 3 later than No. 2?
11. Can you find evidence that the room is fairly warm?
12. Between which two pictures was the spoon first touched?

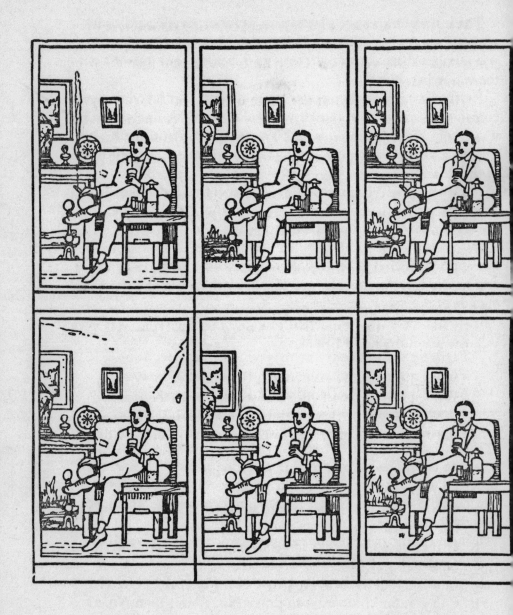

TIME IN REILLY'S LIFE

These six pictures are placed in a random, haphazard order without regard for the time or the date they were made. Can you number them correctly from 1 to 6, basing your answers on the following data?

Reilly was a bachelor in moderate though comfortable circumstances, and was about 28 years old when the first picture was taken. He frequently spent his evenings at home alone, sitting in a chair before the fireplace around ten-thirty, with a highball and a cigar.

He was a man of very regular, conservative habits—which accounts for his being shown always in the same position, in the same chair, over a period of 20 years.

Of course we see him only on certain evenings when he is home alone, buried in deep thought. He wasn't *always* like this, and he *did* have more than one suit of clothes. But that part is outside of our story. . . .

Figure 1 shows Reilly at 10:30 P.M., Jan. 10, 1902.
Figure 2 shows Reilly at 10:31 P.M., Jan. 10, 1902.
Figure 3 shows Reilly at 10:50 P.M., Jan. 10, 1902.
Figure 4 shows Reilly at 10:30 P.M., July 10, 1912.
Figure 5 shows Reilly at 10:30 P.M., July 10, 1914.
Figure 6 shows Reilly at 11:00 P.M., Jan. 10, 1922.

There is conclusive evidence in each picture which fixes the time and the date in relation to the other pictures. There is only one possible order in which the six pictures can be arranged correctly in TIME.

Can you number all six in their proper order, and give all the reasons why you are positive about your solution?

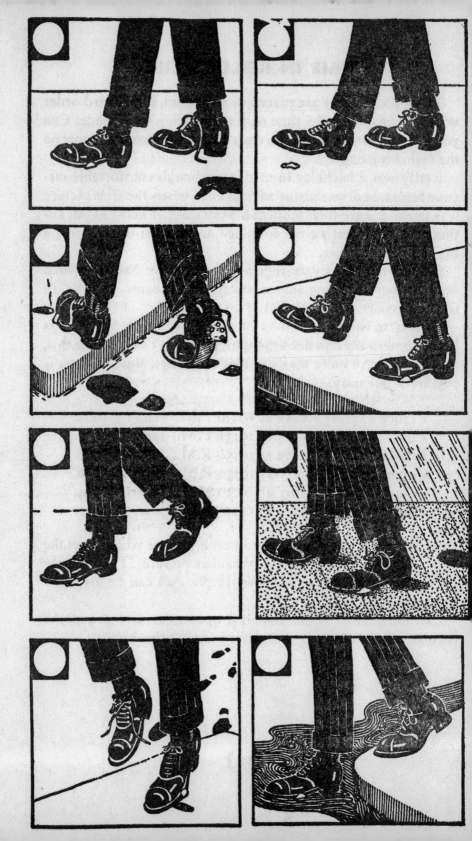

THE MARCH OF TIME

The eight sketches opposite show "Legs" Walker in search of a job. They are arranged in haphazard order, but there is positive evidence of their only possible time-sequence. Observing the chewing-gum, the cigar, and some other things, see if you can number the circles correctly from 1 to 8, and then use your logic and reasoning powers on the questions below.

After you have numbered the circles, see if you can answer these questions correctly.

1. Tell something that "Legs" did between Pictures 7 and 8.
2. Tell two ways you know by No. 8 that "Legs" is tired.
3. Give two reasons why you think he is a poor man.
4. Give three reasons why you judge him to be careless.
5. Tell two ways you know the footprints belong to "Legs."
6. Was it a sunny day before the shower came up?
7. How can you be sure that Picture No. 3 is later in time than Picture No. 2?
8. How do you know that "Legs" hasn't yet stepped on the sidewalk in Picture No. 5?
9. Tell why you think a longer time elapsed between Nos. 7 and 8, than between any other two consecutive pictures.

WET OR DRY?

Here are some mixed up pages from the diary of Samuel Pepys as he might have written it if the old gentleman had taken one cocktail too many. The statements are all mixed up as you can see and it is up to you to number them consecutively from 1 to 19 in the one and only logical order that is possible. After each statement write its number in the correct TIME order. The first three have been done to start you off:

a. I ran the water. ....
b. I wet my shoes. ....
c. I grabbed a towel. ....
d. I did not wet my shoes. ....
e. I dried my shoes. ....
f. I put on rubbers. ....
g. I took a shower. ....
h. I went back home. ....
i. I went out again. ....
j. I started dressing. ....
k. I got up. ....3...........
l. I woke up. ....1.......
m. I walked in the rain. ....
n. I put on my socks. ....
o. I went outdoors. ....
p. I finished dressing. ....
q. I put on my shoes. ....
r. I dried myself. ....
s. I sat up. ....2...........

"ENCLOSED PLEASE FIND . . ."

Here is a mail order time sequence puzzle similar to the one on the previous page. See how fast you can straighten it out by numbering each sentence in its proper time sequence—just as you did in the WET OR DRY puzzle. Number 1 and number 19 are done for you.

a. He received the catalogue. ....1..........
b. He opened the package. ....
c. He tried out a second. ....
d. He wrote for a dozen. ....
e. He mailed the letter. ....
f. He found all twelve. ....
g. He looked up the price. ....
h. He awaited the package. ....
i. He used every one. ....
j. He sealed the letter. ....
k. He saw what he wanted. ....
l. He counted the contents. ....
m. He enclosed a dollar. ....
n. He opened the catalogue. ....
o. He tried one out. ....
p. He received the package. ....
q. He used up another. ....
r. He turned to the price list. ....
s. He ordered some more. ....19........

HOW MUCH DO YOU KNOW?

Tests of Your General Knowledge

How many questions in this section can you answer correctly? Groups A, B, C and D are not as easy as they look and we advise you to look before you leap. If you get 20 out of the 25 you are in the excellent class; 17 to 20 is very good; 12 to 17 is good.

Everything in this section may be played as oral or written games in large groups.

TRUE OR FALSE?

Group A.

	True	False
1. Carson City, Nevada, is west of Los Angeles, California.	....	....
2. You cannot freeze water while it is boiling.	....	....
3. Hongkong is a city in China.	....	....
4. In summer the days grow shorter and the nights grow longer.	....	....
5. No part of Canada is South of the U. S.	....	....
6. The Bible says that Jonah was swallowed by a whale.	....	....
7. The earth is nearer the sun in summer than it is in winter.	....	....
8. There is no snow in the region of the equator.	....	....
9. Mother Goose was an imaginary character.	....	....
10. A blind worm is a little blind creature like a mole.	....	....
11. The freezing point of water is 32° Fahrenheit.	....	....
12. A guinea is worth more than a pound.	....	....
13. Pekin is the capital of China.	....	....
14. The word most used over the telephone is "hello."	....	....
15. The Wright Brothers built the first airplane.	....	....
16. There is a country between France and Spain.	....	....
17. A cork ball 6 feet in diameter weighs more than 1000 pounds.	....	....
18. The Battle of Bunker Hill did not take place on Bunker Hill.	....	....
19. The North Star is directly over the North Pole.	....	....
20. Moths eat holes in clothes.	....	....
21. A knot is a little more than a mile.	....	....
22. A lady-bird is an insect.	....	....
23. An orrery is a place where birds are kept.	....	....
24. Sydney is the capital of Australia.	....	....
25. Greenland is a colonial possession of Denmark.	....	....

TRUE OR FALSE?

Group B.

	True	False
1. It is impossible to go in the opposite direction by going in the same direction.	....	....
2. The earthworm has a nervous system.	....	....
3. My wife's sister's husband is my mother-in-law's son.	....	....
4. The five-cent piece is mostly nickel.	....	....
5. The rainbow contains all the colors.	....	....
6. Caesar was the first Emperor of Rome.	....	....
7. Trotsky was the most prominent figure at Lenin's funeral.	....	....
8. Marconi did not discover the wireless waves.	....	....
9. St. Patrick was not an Irishman.	....	....
10. Camel's hair brushes are made from Camel's hair.	....	....
11. Moles are blind.	....	....
12. A word which best describes jute is hemp.	....	....
13. The compass needle points to the North Pole.	....	....
14. The United States has a larger area than Brazil.	....	....
15. It is farther by water from Paris, France, to Buenos Aires, S. A., than it is from El Paso, Texas, to Buenos Aires, S. A.	....	....
16. The sun always sets in the west.	....	....
17. George Washington was the first president of the U. S.	....	....
18. Cream is heavier than milk.	....	....
19. Reno is the capital of Nevada.	....	....
20. Benjamin Franklin invented the harmonica.	....	....
21. Betsy Ross made the first American flag.	....	....
22. Uraeus is a medical term.	....	....
23. Texas is more than 50 miles from Colorado.	....	....
24. Puccini wrote *Madame Butterfly*.	....	....
25. A cuttle fish is not a fish.	....	....

TRUE OR FALSE?

Group C.

	True	False
1. Tegucigalpa is a Spanish disease.	....	....
2. The most southerly city in the U. S. is Brownsville, Texas.	....	....
3. Lead is heavier than gold.	....	....
4. Venus is the brightest star in the sky.	....	....
5. Columbus discovered America.	....	....
6. The Declaration of Independence was signed July 4th 1776.	....	....
7. Any wood is lighter than any metal.	....	....
8. Lapland is in northern Greenland.	....	....
9. A kiwi is a wingless bird.	....	....
10. Only female mosquitoes bite.	....	....
11. Morse invented the telegraph.	....	....
12. The electro magnet is the most useful invention of modern times.	....	....
13. The English Horn is made of wood.	....	....
14. Every year which is divisible by 4 is a leap year.	....	....
15. The city of London is less than two square miles in area.	....	....
16. Nicotine is a brownish oily liquid.	....	....
17. Tin cans are made out of tin.	....	....
18. Bombay is the capital of India.	....	....
19. January 1st 1900 was the first day of the 20th Century	....	....
20. The 30 Years War lasted 34 years.	....	....
21. The term "midsummer" refers to the middle of summer.	....	....
22. It is impossible to have a noiseless explosion.	....	....
23. Steam is invisible.	....	....
24. A spider is not an insect.	....	....
25. Cleopatra was an Egyptian.	....	....

TRUE OR FALSE?

Group D.

	True	False
1. A vang is a rope.	....	....
2. A sunflower always faces the sun.	....	....
3. Playing discords on a newly tuned piano will put it out of tune.	....	....
4. The automobile was invented shortly after the Civil War.	....	....
5. A hurricane nearly always travels slowly.	....	....
6. An Analemma is a South American animal.	....	....
7. A 7 sided figure is called a "Septagon."	....	....
8. Germany is a republic.	....	....
9. Jesus was born in the year 1.	....	....
10. The leaning tower of Pisa is not in Pisa at all.	....	....
11. Ice is often called hard water.	....	....
12. In his lifetime the average man travels millions of miles.	....	....
13. A mantissa is part of an insect.	....	....
14. Insole is a kind of fish.	....	....
15. Catgut comes from the intestines of cats.	....	....
16. If life on the moon were possible, telephones would be useless there.	....	....
17. Richard Wagner wrote Lohengrin.	....	....
18. Sapphires are not always blue.	....	....
19. A unicorn is a mythical animal.	....	....
20. Sheet lightning is different from fork lightning.	....	....
21. Mount Blanc is in Switzerland.	....	....
22. Sealing wax is not wax.	....	....
23. Beer has been known since the year 1.	....	....
24. Laughing hyenas actually laugh.	....	....
25. An English countess is the wife of an English count.	....	....

NAME FIVE

1. Name the quintuplets:

....

....

....

....

....

2. Name the 5 Great Lakes:

....

....

....

....

3. Name 5 planets:

....

....

....

....

4. Name 5 infant prodigies in music:

....

....

....

....

5. Name 5 Mother Goose rhymes beginning with "Little":

....

....

....

....

6. Name 5 dirigibles that have been wrecked:

....

....

....

....

7. Name 5 musical instruments beginning with the letter T:

....

....

....

....

....

8. Name 5 proverbs about time:

....

....

....

....

....

9. Name 5 famous men named Smith:

....

....

....

....

....

10. Name 5 symbols of Good Luck:

....

....

....

....

....

11. Name 5 animals peculiar to Australia:

....

....

....

....

12. Name 5 things that are considered unlucky to do:

....

....

....

....

NAME TEN

1. Name 10 brands of cigarettes:

-------------------------------- --------------------------------
-------------------------------- --------------------------------
-------------------------------- --------------------------------
-------------------------------- --------------------------------
-------------------------------- --------------------------------

2. Name 10 musical instruments beginning with the letter C:

-------------------------------- --------------------------------
-------------------------------- --------------------------------
-------------------------------- --------------------------------
-------------------------------- --------------------------------
-------------------------------- --------------------------------

3. Name 10 countries in South America:

-------------------------------- --------------------------------
-------------------------------- --------------------------------
-------------------------------- --------------------------------
-------------------------------- --------------------------------
-------------------------------- --------------------------------

4. Name 10 twentieth century Celebrities whose last name begins with Z:

-------------------------------- --------------------------------
-------------------------------- --------------------------------
-------------------------------- --------------------------------
-------------------------------- --------------------------------
-------------------------------- --------------------------------

5. Name the 10 largest cities in the United States:

-------------------------------- --------------------------------
-------------------------------- --------------------------------
-------------------------------- --------------------------------
-------------------------------- --------------------------------
-------------------------------- --------------------------------

6. Name the 10 largest cities in the world:

-------------------------------- --------------------------------
-------------------------------- --------------------------------
-------------------------------- --------------------------------
-------------------------------- --------------------------------
-------------------------------- --------------------------------

GENERAL TEST

(Par: 14)

1. Use the same letter 14 times to make sense from the following:

    thsthrswrsnvrndnwndls

2. Just what does the following ungrammatical sentence mean?

    Don't never say I didn't never give you nothing!

3. A word of nine letters has only one vowel. What is the word?

    ----

4. Only one statement in the following is true. Which is it?
    1. Nicotine is a brownish oily liquid.
    2. A knot is a nautical mile.
    3. An even number can be a prime number.
    4. Thomas Whitney invented the telephone.
    5. January 1st 1900 was the first day of the 20th Century.

5. In the number below put a 4 over every 3 that is followed by a 4 and a 3 under every 4 that is followed by a 3:

    75348654394563283475237343259879240435234 75

6. Punctuate and make sense from the following:
    Smith while I wrote wrote wrote wrote wrote I wrote

7. Describe something in three words using only the first 4 letters of the alphabet.

    ----

8. Show by the use of the words "friend" and "enemy" how a minus times a minus may be proved to equal a plus.

    ----

9. What common word contains one vowel repeated 6 times?

    ----

10. List 8 ways of spelling the sound o as in the word "no."
    1. ---------------------   5. ---------------------
    2. ---------------------   6. ---------------------
    3. ---------------------   7. ---------------------
    4. ---------------------   8. ---------------------

[128]

11. I multiply two numbers together and get their sum; I divide one into the other and get ¼th their product. What are the numbers?

12. The first letter of a 5-letter word is the last letter of the alphabet and vice versa. What is the word?

....

13. My father's uncle's nephew is your son. What relation are you to me?

14. He begins a word and he ends it. What's the word?

15. Which pair of words contains the same letters? Underline them:

MEDALS	SELDOM
SMOLDS	MOLTES
MODELS	SOLEMN
STOLEN	SMOTES

16. Fill in the blanks:

   verb is to .... as .... is to word.

17. If a minute is more than an hour don't write the word "second" unless there are as many seconds in a minute as there are minutes in an hour in which case write the word "minute."

....

18. What is the largest possible number that can be written with 3 digits? What is the smallest number that can be written this way?

   Largest:.....................   Smallest:.....................

19. Johnson travels as far as the average commuter every day. He doesn't ride in a train, an automobile, a carriage, a trolley car or anything that travels on wheels. He has never been in an airplane and won't travel on boats of any description. He doesn't ride on any animal and he doesn't walk or run or use his legs in his travels. How does Johnson accomplish this remarkable feat?

20. What is wrong with this:

   "He proposed to me on a beautiful moonlight night. The next day I was so thrilled that I completely forgot to watch the sun eclipse."

HOW MUCH DO YOU KNOW?

Group I.

(Count 4 points for each correct answer. Par: 60)

1. What is meant by T.V.A., C.C.C. and N.R.A.? ....
2. Who wrote the music for Porgy and Bess? ....
3. What major disaster occurred in East Texas in March, 1937? ....
4. What is meant by the expression "packing the courts"? ....
5. What star is the most important for determining latitude? ....
6. Who wrote the opera "Fidelio"? ....
7. Where did the month of October get its name? ....
8. What is an electron? ....
9. What is the significance in the saying "As Maine goes, so goes Vermont"? ....
10. What is "garrote"? ....
11. What is the greatest example of musical collaboration in all light opera? ....
12. Where is Point Barrow? ....
13. What is meant by "anschluss"? ....
14. Who was the "Wild Bull of the Pampas"? ....
15. What two world-famous characters were killed in an airplane wreck in Alaska? ....
16. What is the second largest city in England? ....
17. What best seller has broken all records by selling more than a million copies? ....
18. What is meant by a latus rectum of a parabola? ....
19. Who wrote "Cimarron"? ....
20. Who sighed for "more worlds to conquer"? ....
21. Who said "Give me liberty or give me death"? ....
22. How many years did Rip Van Winkle sleep? ....
23. How does an explorer know when he is at the North or South Pole? ....
24. What great scientist was exiled from Nazi Germany because he was a Jew? ....
25. What does S. P. C. A. stand for? ....

HOW MUCH DO YOU KNOW?

Group 2.

(Count 4 points for each correct answer. Par: 65)

1. What government violated the Treaty of Versailles and the Pact of Locarno? ....
2. Who wrote "Of Human Bondage"? ....
3. In what century did Sir Isaac Newton live? ....
4. Who was the Chief Justice of the Supreme Court before Hughes? ....
5. Where do mosquitoes spend their early youth? ....
6. What is meant by "ibid."? ....
7. How many articles are in a "baker's dozen"? ....
8. What is the only state that touches only one state? ....
9. Of what use is litmus paper? ....
10. What is the normal temperature of the human body? ....
11. Is latitude 40° north, longitude 40° west a good place to build a house and why? ....
12. What is meant by faulty progression? ....
13. Who said "Let them eat cake"? ....
14. What are the first three words of the Duke of Windsor's farewell speech? ....
15. Who are the Leftists in Spain? ....
16. Who was supposed to have said "There's one born every minute"? ....
17. What is the largest denomination of U. S. paper currency? ....
18. Where did the first battle of the World War take place? ....
19. What great English poet deliberately sacrificed his eyesight for the sake of his country? ....
20. Who was Oliver Cromwell? ....
21. What strip of foreign land divides Nazi Germany in the east? ....
22. What is a "berceuse"? ....
23. Who wrote "Ethan Frome"? ....
24. What is meant by the expression "raison d'être"? ....
25. What is a "ghost writer"? ....

HOW MUCH DO YOU KNOW?

Group 3.

(Count 4 points for each correct answer. Par: 70)

1. Who were the three great "B's" of music? ....
2. When did John D. Rockefeller die? ....
3. What is the third largest city in the world? ....
4. What is a cedilla? ....
5. What is meant by a morganatic marriage? ....
6. Who is Ogden Nash? ....
7. What is the capital of Persia? ....
8. What is the capital of Finland? ....
9. What is a howdah? ....
10. Who is Pooh Bah? ....
11. What island lies Southeast of Africa? ....
12. What is meant by specific gravity? ....
13. What is "eminent domain"? ....
14. Where is Devil's Island? ....
15. What famous playwright wrote "Peter Pan"? ....
16. How many centimeters are there in an inch? ....
17. What is an isosceles triangle? ....
18. Which is heavier, lead or platinum? ....
19. What is "hara-kiri"? ....
20. When was the Treaty of Versailles signed? ....
21. Who is the cartoonist who created "The Timid Soul"? ....
22. Where are the Thousand Islands? ....
23. What is meant by "vulnerable" in contract bridge? ....
24. Who is Dr. Dafoe? ....
25. What is the poisonous element in paris green? ....

HOW MUCH DO YOU KNOW?

Group 4.

(Count 4 for each correct answer. Par: 50)

1. Where is Latvia with respect to Poland? ....
2. What is the female of deer? ....
3. What is an oboe? ....
4. How far up is the stratosphere? ....
5. What was Houdini's correct name? ....
6. Name a well known spiral nebula. ....
7. If the compass were taken to the North Pole, in which direction would it point? ....
8. Name four citrus fruits. ....
9. What is a ling? ....
10. Who were the Niebelungs? ....
11. By whom is the Pope chosen? ....
12. Who said "We should be too proud to fight"? ....
13. What is a catenary? ....
14. What Match King was connected with an international swindle? ....
15. Who was Secretary of War in 1917? ....
16. What musical composer's name is associated with George Sand? ....
17. What is the N. Y. A.? ....
18. Where is the original Rialto? ....
19. What is the population (approximately) of Los Angeles? ....
20. What cigarette manufacturer recently conducted a $200,-000 prize contest? ....
21. What is a thermostat? ....
22. Who is Dale Carnegie? ....
23. What is meant by a lathe? ....
24. Which city is larger, Chicago or Paris? ....
25. What ship was Captain Reese commander of? ....

Part IV

30

ORAL GAMES THAT REQUIRE NO PREPARATION

---

7 *Best Adult Game Suggestions*
Nos. 3, 10, 11, 18, 22, 23 and 30

7 *Best Young Folks Game Suggestions*
Nos. 1, 8, 12, 13, 16, 28 and 29

1. ALPHABET GAME

Arrange the guests in a circle which shall include you. Start the game off by saying the following:

"Yesterday I was at Mr. Jones' house for dinner and I had Artichokes." (Or some other edible beginning with A.)

The person sitting to the right of you now repeats what you just said, adding some edible beginning with B. For example:

"Yesterday I was at Mr. Jones' house for dinner and I had Artichokes and Beans."

The next person now repeats this, adding an edible beginning with C. For example:

"Yesterday I was at Mr. Jones' house for dinner and I had Artichokes, Beans and Cabbage."

Each person in turn repeats what the previous person has just said and adds the name of some edible beginning with the next letter in the alphabet. As the game progresses it is not necessary to say "Yesterday I was at Mr. Jones' house" each time. The players may merely start off with "I had Artichokes, Beans, Cabbage, Doughnuts, Eels, etc." but each player MUST include the entire list up to his letter (in alphabetical order) and then add his particular edible. The player who misses any of the names on the list or hesitates too long is declared out of the game. The player remaining the longest in the game wins.

2. ALPHABET MEMORY GAME

This is a lot of fun though it becomes quite difficult after a while and there are very few people who can complete the entire alphabet.

Arrange the guests in a circle which shall include you and start the game off by mentioning any word at all beginning with A. Suppose you say "Africa."

The person immediately to your right repeats your word, adding another word beginning with A. He may say "Africa, atlas."

The person to his right now repeats these two words and adds another word beginning with A. He may say "Africa, atlas, addition." This goes around the circle until it comes back to you. You now start off with the letter B which goes around the circle and when it comes back to you start again with the letter C and so on.

This game is as difficult as the number of people in it. If there are ten people playing, there will be 10 A's, 10 B's, etc., so that by the time you reach the letter M you will have to remember 120 words and repeat them in the order that they are given in the game. Of course you will always hear them again and again so you will get to know them from memory, but nevertheless you have to keep your wits about you.

The player who misses any of the words is out of the game. The player who stays in the game the longest wins.

Code Games

The four code games that follow are all fascinating and full of mystery. After doing any one of them a few times to the amazement of your guests get them to try to tell you how it is done. In a few cases you will be safe in offering a prize to anyone who can correctly explain the code, because, simple as the code is when you know it, it is just as difficult to guess!

In all these code games, you must have a confederate who knows the code as well as you do. You and your wife or husband can do it together. If you care to, you can select a confederate from the guests, take him quietly inside without anyone knowing it, and show him the code. Of course it is preferable to have some one of the guests do it with you—it won't look quite so "fishy" to the other guests.

3. CODE GAME A.

Code game No. 1 is easy when you know how to do it, but it is almost impossible to decipher. It goes like this:

Send your confederate out of the room and tell the remaining guests to take the name of any prominent person. Suppose they take President Roosevelt. You call your confederate in and say something to this effect:

"Nice Raspberries."

and then blink once. Your confederate will immediately say

"Roosevelt"

Now what have nice raspberries and an unnoticed blink got to do with Roosevelt? The answer is nothing—that's just where the fun comes in! The clue is in the initial letters and the number of blinks! The blinks represent vowels. 1 blink is A, two blinks, E; three blinks, I; four blinks, O and five blinks, U. The consonants are the initial letters of the words. We thus have

N (for nice) R (for raspberries) and A for 1 blink

N R A immediately suggests Roosevelt!

If the guests had taken Lindbergh you might say: Wisconsin, and blink twice. This obviously spells WE to your confederate —and WE will always stand for Lindbergh as long as he lives.

Notice that you never take the *name* of the prominent person. You choose something *definitely connected with that person that will immediately suggest him*. If Einstein were taken the word would naturally be *Relativity* and might go something like this:

Rats – – – (blink twice) – – – Love – – – (blink once)

Tonsils – – – and by this time your confederate would have spelled out RELAT . . . and immediately concluded RELATIVITY and said "EINSTEIN."

4. CODE GAME B.

Send your confederate out of the room and choose any object in the room. Call in your confederate and, assuming a pose of deep concentration, point to the various objects in the room *without saying a word!* When you finally point to the object selected your confederate will say "That's it!"

This code will completely mystify everyone in the room! After all, not a word or a look passed between you and your confederate. How on earth is it done?

It is so simple that it is laughable! You merely agree beforehand with your confederate on the previous object—and that

[138]

is all there is to it. The object *just before* the one in question can be *any one* of the following:

a. Any object with legs such as a chair, table, piano, person, dog, etc.
b. Any object which is black or in which black predominates.
c. Any object made of wood or in which wood predominates.
d. Any object which is circular such as an ash tray, a round table, a half dollar, etc.

Remember to agree on *ONE* of these four. If you agree on *a* then be sure to point to a table or a chair *just before* you point to the object selected and be sure NOT to point to a chair, table or anything else that has legs until that time.

If you agree on *b* don't point to anything that is black until you are ready and then be sure that the next object you point to is the selected one. The same is true for *c* and *d*.

You will probably have to do this a number of times and it may happen that your guests will want to choose the objects to which you point. In this case say "they're directing me" to your confederate when he enters and *put your hand in your pocket* when pointing to the object selected.

5. CODE GAME C.

Without anyone noticing it, take one of your guests aside and tell him this code. Then tell everyone that one of the guests in the room will point to a person in the room and, in spite of the fact that you will be in the next room, out of sight of everyone with the door partially shut, you will shout out the name of the person! The only thing necessary to do this is to be in "cahoots" with your partner.

Now go in the next room and partially close the door so that everyone will know that you cannot see what is going on. As your partner (confederate) points to the various people in the room he will holler out from time to time: "are you in cahoots?" and you can either say "yes" or "no" depending on when you want him to start. As soon as you say "yes" you can depend on it that the next person who speaks (being the host or hostess you will know the voice) will be the person to whom your partner will point. You then shout out his or her name and amaze your guests.

The code is therefore: the person pointed to is always the first person who speaks after you have said "yes" to the question "are you in cahoots?".

6. CODE GAME D.

This is the most astounding code of them all and because it is so mystifying it requires a little memory work on your part and the part of your confederate. Your confederate in this case should be either your husband or wife, or your brother or sister or some one member of your family whom you see every day and with whom you can practice.

The code will enable you to tell the dates on coins or the amount of money in peoples' pockets or what colors are selected while you are blindfolded in another room with the door partially shut.

The code was made up by Robert Heller, a famous magician. Don't attempt to change the code words. They have been tested and have proved to be the easiest. Learn them thoroughly before the party. Let your confederate do the same. Learn to send as well as to receive.

Here is the code. Memorize it thoroughly:

NUMBER	CODE WORD	COLOR
1	Say or Speak	Blue
2	Look or Let	Green
3	Can or Can't	Yellow
4	Do or Don't	Orange
5	Will or Won't	Red
6	What	Black
7	Please	White
8	Are	Grey
9	Now	Brown
0	Quick	Gold

In guessing the dates on coins it is only necessary to give the last two numbers since fully 95% of all coins today are less than 37 years old. The first two digits will invariably be 19 so that

[140]

all you need do is say two sentences the first word of each sentence to be a code word.

Now, you go out of the room. Your confederate asks for a coin. Someone hands him a quarter dated 1913. All he need do is flash 13 to you which he does as follows:

"*Speak* up now. *Can* you tell the date?"

You hear *Speak* and *Can,* which means 1 and 3 and you holler back 19*13*.

Now someone else hands your confederate a half dollar dated 1924. He then says:

"*Look* out for this one. *Don't* be fooled by it!"

You hear *Look* and *Don't,* which means 2 and 4 and you holler back 1924.

In case your confederate does come across a coin in the 1800's he will *cough* before he says anything to you. When you hear him cough you will know that the coin begins with 18. . . .

Of course this code is good for guessing the amount of money in a guest's pocket. In this case the last two numbers are cents. If your confederate says "How much money has Harry?" and then says: "*Will* you tell me as quickly as you can? *Please* don't take so long. *Will* you let us have the answer?" you know that Harry must have $5.75!

Only one sentence is necessary for naming a chosen color. For example:

"*Can't* you guess?" is Yellow.

"*Look* carefully" is Green.

7. NAME FIVE OR TEN

Use questions given on pages 125–7 orally instead of in written form. Seat your guests in a semicircle and start with the person on the extreme left. Ask him to name the 5 Great Lakes. If he fails he is out of the game and the next person gets the same question. Proceed in this fashion going through the entire list given. There is certainly nothing to prevent you from making up a list of your own such as "Name 10 plays of Shakespeare, Name 10 birds . . . etc."

8. TWENTY QUESTIONS NEW STYLE

Read the following to your guests and bet with any one of them or all of them that they cannot guess what you have in mind in less than 35 questions. The chances are you will always win.

The thing I have in mind is neither animal, vegetable nor mineral—nor is it abstract.

It is totally useless to me yet I could not live without it. It belongs to me although nobody gave it to me and I didn't buy it, borrow it, or steal it.

I am always losing it but it doesn't worry me because it is always returned to me. If it fell off the roof of a tall building on to a hard city pavement it would not break or even crack.

Although I can see it and touch it, I can't feel it. It never makes a noise and never does any work although, on special occasions it has been known to open things.

Dogs have it, ostriches have it too, but fish only have it in very shallow water.

(Make up a lot more things to tell your guests about this mysterious thing. *Let them ask as many questions as they like* but don't tell too much and, above all don't mention the changeable *length* unless you want to give the thing away.)

THE THING YOU HAVE IN MIND IS YOUR SHADOW!

The photo-electric cell doors are opened by letting your shadow fall on the photo-electric cell.

9. TWENTY QUESTIONS—FRENCH METHOD

This is played just like Twenty Questions. Everyone is seated in a circle and the guesser stands in the center and asks each person a question in turn. All questions must have a "yes" or "no" answer and each person, of course, answers truthfully. The game is played once only and will prove to be a lot of fun for everyone except the guesser. The reason the guesser finds such difficulty in guessing the thing chosen is because it is always "the person on my right" and the guesser goes round and round, never arriving at a satisfactory answer until he sees the trick and asks "is it the person on your right?"

10. YOU DON'T KNOW WHAT YOU ARE TALKING ABOUT

Arrange the guests in a semicircle and tell them that you are going to select six speakers from among them. Each speaker is to talk for three minutes on a subject about which he knows absolutely nothing! He must keep talking on this subject and the more nonsense he talks, the better and funnier it will be for his audience who are encouraged to applaud or boo as they see fit. In case you want a few subjects to start off the game, try the following:

1. The sewer system in Moscow.
2. Duties of a tea taster's assistant in Ceylon.
3. What happens to all the pins, needles and umbrellas.
4. How many dadoes there are on the average lino and why there are not more.
5. Why seaweed is impractical for stuffing upholstery.

The winner of this game is the one who, by popular vote, talks the most foolishness. Make up your own subjects.

11. JUST TO MAKE CONVERSATION

This is one of the funniest games in the book and is sure to produce a deluge of laughter every time it is played. Select a man and a girl from your guests and tell them that they are going to hold a conversation together. Now tell them to leave the room and while they are out agree on two sentences which shall be *as opposite as possible*. One of these will be given to the man who must repeat it *word for word* in his conversation with the girl, without her noticing it. The other will be given to the girl who must repeat it *word for word* in her conversation with the man, without his noticing it. Of course neither one knows what the other's sentence is, yet they are both on the lookout for something unusual. Whoever gets away with his sentence without the other knowing it wins.

Here is a typical pair of sentences:

Mr. Smith's sentence: The sabbath is the golden clasp that binds together the volume of the week.

Miss Jones' sentence: Pickling beets in Hongkong is not as easy as you think it is.

When the conversation starts Mr. Smith will constantly be leading Miss Jones into religious subjects until he can put over his little sentence unnoticed by Miss Jones. Miss Jones, on the other hand will try to take Mr. Smith with her to China where she can introduce the pickling of beets and get off her sentence unnoticed by Mr. Smith.

Here are a few other suggestions for other sentences:

Boy's sentence: Never show an ostrich that you are afraid of him.

Girl's sentence: I always fry everything in lard.

Boy's sentence: They say that one should feed a cold and starve a fever.

Girl's sentence: Einstein is the world's greatest scientist today.

12. TONGUE TWISTERS

Offer a prize to anyone who can say *all* of the following tongue twisters perfectly in the quickest possible time:

1. What a shame such a shapely sash should show such shabby stilted stitches!

2. The Leith police beseecheth us.
3. Miss Shirley sold Mrs. Smith's fresh fish sauce.
4. Good blood, bad blood. (say this 8 times very quickly)
5. Miss Smith's fish sauce shop seldom sells shell fish.

13. BUZZ

Arrange the guests in a circle and starting with number 1 tell them to count—each one saying the next highest number, but instead of saying the number 7 or any multiple of 7 like 14, 21, 28, etc. the word *"Buzz"* must be substituted. The counting must proceed as quickly as is possible and anyone failing to say *"Buzz"* in place of 7 or its multiples is out of the game.

14. WRONG IS RIGHT

Form two lines, one of girls and the other of boys. Have them stand up and face one another. The object of this game is to answer questions incorrectly and anyone giving the correct answer must sit down.

The boy at the head of the line starts by asking the girl opposite him a question. She must answer immediately and if she answers that question correctly she must sit down and be declared out of the game. If she gives the wrong answer she must ask the next boy in line (the second boy) another question and he, after answering it wrong, asks the girl opposite him another question—and so on down the line and back again. The winner is the one who remains standing the longest. The answers to all questions must be immediate—any hesitation puts a player out of the game.

15. ENDLESS CHAIN OF CITIES

Arrange the guests in a circle, which shall include you, and let anyone start by naming an American city beginning with A. Suppose he says "Albany." Albany ends in Y so the next person must name a city or State beginning with Y. Suppose he says

"Youngstown." Youngstown ends in N so the next person must name a city beginning with N and so on. All answers must be immediate and anyone hesitating or failing to follow in the regular order is declared out of the game.

16. POOR PUSSY

This is an old but very amusing game and never fails to create shrieks of laughter.

Line up the guests so that the girls face the boys. The lines should be about six feet apart. The first boy in line starts by going over to the first girl, kneeling in front of her and saying "meow" three times. The girl must stroke the boy's head each time he says "meow" and say "Poor Pussy" without smiling. If the girl does this successfully in spite of the laughter from the rest of the guests, she goes over to the next boy in line kneels and says "meow" three times. This time the boy must stroke the girl's head and say "Poor Pussy" just as before.

The game continues until some serious minded winner has been able to keep a straight face each time his turn came.

17. GHOSTS

Divide your guests into two equal parts or sides and let them sit facing one another. Make a man the "captain" of part 1 and a girl the "captain" of part 2. The man begins the game with a letter—any letter that comes into his head—suppose it is K. The girl then adds another letter with the idea of starting a word which someone else has to finish. She might say N, having in mind the word "Knot." Now the next person on the opposite (man's) side adds a letter. He may say I instead of O with the word "Knife" in mind. This goes on from one side to the other until a word is spelled and the person who adds the completing letter to the word is declared "out once." If he is out three times he is a ghost and nobody must talk to him although he may talk to everyone and try to get them to talk to him. Anyone who talks to a "ghost" becomes one himself.

Of course the idea of the game is to try to keep from ending a word but sometimes it is impossible. If anyone adds a letter to the other letters without a definite word in mind he is open to challenge and if he can't name the word he has in mind he is declared "out once."

18. PROVERBS

Select someone to leave the room and while he is out decide on a proverb. Suppose the proverb is "A rolling stone gathers no moss." Everyone having agreed on this proverb, the person out of the room is called back, and it is up to him, through questioning each guest in turn, to find out what the proverb is. It is the duty of each guest, in responding to the questions, to see that one of the words in the proverb is included in his reply. For example, the questioner might ask the first guest,

"Is this an easy proverb?" His reply would be, "It is *a* very easy proverb." The next question might be, "Do I know it?" The second reply would be, "You do. It is as easy as *rolling* off a log." The answer to the third question should contain the word *'Stone.'* The answer to the fourth question should contain the word *'Gathers.'* Be sure to choose a proverb which is not too obvious, otherwise the guesser will arrive at the proverb too quickly. Of course you must not emphasize the key word in any way when you answer.

19. ONE MINUTE TO GO

This is one of the most fascinating games we know. You, as the host or hostess, hold a watch in your hand and tell your guests that you are going to name a letter (not 'X'). After you name the letter, the person on your right must name as many words as he can, beginning with that letter, within a minute. It is up to you to be the time keeper and scorer.

Suppose you name 'H', as soon as you are ready to start, say "Go!" and the person on your right will start pouring out words beginning with 'H', like 'hat', 'heaven', 'hold', 'hemp', etc. You must keep track of the words and, at the end of a minute, stop him. If he gets more than 23 words, he is doing very well. When this is finished, some other letter is called for, and the same thing takes place. The one who gets the most words, of course wins the game. Plurals, or variations of the same word, are not allowed.

20. ADVERBS

Send one person out of the room and let those remaining choose some adverb. Suppose they choose 'amiably.' The person out of the room is called in, and must ask each guest a question in turn. Each guest must answer his question "in the manner of the adverb." The first guest might answer it with smiles. The second guest might answer the next question in the most pleasant manner possible, putting himself out in every way. It is up to the questioner to guess the adverb from the manner in which the guests answer.

Naturally, if the adverb were 'angrily,' each guest would tend to storm about and fly into a rage in answering his respective question.

21. ENDLESS STORY CHAIN

Arrange the guests in a circle, and have one guest start off by telling a story—any story whatever. He may continue as long as a minute and he must not end the story—very unexpectedly he must stop abruptly and touch the person on his right, who must continue the story in his, or her, own particular style. Some awfully queer themes can result from this, and the story must be kept going until everyone in the circle has had a chance to have his say.

22. OPPOSITES

Arrange the guests in a semicircle and stand in front of one of them with a chair in back of you. Before you start to hold a conversation with him tell him that while you are talking to him, he must do *exactly the opposite* from what you do. If you sit down, he must stand up. If you raise your right leg, he must raise his left leg. If you both happen to have hats, he must have his on while you have yours off, and vice versa. If you rub your left ear, he must rub his right ear. If you open your mouth wide, he must shut his fairly tightly and mumble his replies, etc. Of course, very few people can do this, so most of your guests will be disqualified, but someone is going to hold out longest, and he will be the winner.

23. ABOUT MYSELF

This game requires a little preparation. Before the guests arrive, write out the names of some outstanding figures, and as soon as they enter, pin one of the names on the back of each guest. The guests then get together and try to establish their identity by questions and answers. For example, the guest with "John Barrymore" on his back (B) meets another guest with "Queen Elizabeth" on her back (E). The conversation might go something like this:

B. "Am I a man?"
E. "Yes, am I?"
B. "No. Am I living?"
E. "Yes, am I?"
B. "No. Am I an American?", etc.

This is an excellent 'ice-breaking' game, as it is a great deal of fun to play.

24. SPELLING BEE A.

Arranged by the hostess. The following are a list of words suggested; read them to your guests:

diocese	iconoclastic	accommodate
evanescent	paraphernalia	erysipelas
precede	referable	occurred
resistible	irritable	irascible
vehement	cemetery	phlegm

25. SPELLING BEE B.

fricassee	effervescence	accede
eleemosynary	manoeuvre	supersede
intolerant	irreconcilable	resuscitate
terrestrial	embarrassed	kaleidoscope
serviceable	assassin	icicle

26. QUOTATIONS

Arrange your guests in a semicircle and, starting at one end, ask that person to complete the quotation which you are about to start. If he completes it correctly he remains in the game and if he doesn't he is out. Now give the next person another quotation to complete and so on until, by the process of elimination, only one person is left. He or she will be the literary light and winner.

Of course it would be best to write down a number of familiar quotations before the guests arrive so that you will have them handy for the game. Always stop them abruptly about at the middle so that the player will have a better chance of answering it. Here are some suggestions:

YOU	PLAYER
"The curfew tolls the knell"	"of parting day"
"Friends, Romans, Countrymen"	"lend me your ears!"
"Give me liberty or"	"give me death."

You can collect hundreds of familiar quotations from the Bible or Shakespeare or famous people in politics.

27. EARTH, AIR, FIRE, WATER

Arrange your guests in a circle. Start off by saying one of the above and either pointing or touching any guest at all. Suppose you say "Air" and touch John Jones. He must immediately respond by naming something that lives or travels in the air. He may say "bird" or "airplane," but he has to say it before you count ten with moderate speed. If he does, you continue. You may say "water" and point to or touch some other guest. His answer must be prompt and correct. He may say "fish," "Boat" or anything that lives in or travels on water.

[150]

There must be no response to the word "Fire." If you say "Fire" and point or touch someone, he must not answer. If he does, he is out. There must be no repetition in this game and if you should say "Air" again and touch somebody else, he cannot say "Bird" or "airplane," he must say "sparrow" or "Zeppelin." If he repeats anything that has been said before, he is out. The last player to remain, of course, is the winner.

28. FORBIDDEN LETTER

Everyone must agree to omit a letter when he answers the questioner, but the questioner need not bother to omit it. The questioner may ask any question he likes, and the person answering it must be sure to use words that do not contain the forbidden letter. Suppose you have all agreed to omit the letter "I" from the answers. The questioner may say to one of the guests, "How do you like this game?" The guest cannot reply, "I like it" or "I do not like it," because these words contain the letter I. His answer could be "Pretty well." If he answers wrong he is out. Each guest in turn is asked a question, *always omitting the forbidden letter in his answer.* After once around a new letter may be chosen.

29. SPOON PICTURES

This is by no means a new game, but no book on games would be complete without it because it is so much fun to play. Two players are in "Cahoots" with one another—that is they know the system, but no one else knows that they know it. You and your friend, for example, might do it together. He is to remain in the room while you go into the next room. He "takes a picture" of one of the guests by holding a tablespoon in front of his or her face and "exposing" it for one or two seconds. He then summons you to come in. You take the spoon, hold it for a minute, examine it, and name the person whose "picture was taken." Everyone is amazed, but the principle is very simple.

Your partner who "takes the picture" sits in the same position as the person whom he "took." If that person has his legs crossed and is smoking a cigarette, your partner does the same. If that person is slouching in his chair, your partner does the same. It is up to you to compare your partner's position with the positions of all the guests and find which one is the "picture one."

30. PROPER NAMES

One of the guests leaves the room while the rest agree on a proper name (the name of a person or place). When he is called back he must ask each person in turn a question in an effort to find out what name was chosen. So far this is just like 20 questions. The difference, however, is in the answers. Unless the name is actually guessed each answer must be in the form:

"No, it is not .... Yes, but it's not ...."

The missing word in the above must begin with the same letter as the name chosen and the answer must be true.

Suppose Beethoven were chosen as the proper name. The questioning might go something like this:

Q. Is it a city in England?
A. No, it is not Birmingham.
Q. Is it a man?
A. Yes, but it's not Bunyon.
Q. Is he alive?
A. No, it is not Byron.
Q. Is he a musician?
A. Yes, but it's not Bach, etc.

Anyone failing to answer correctly is declared out. The winner is, of course, the last one out.

Part V

30
PENCIL AND
PAPER GAMES

---

7 Best Adult Game Suggestions
Nos. 2, 4, 6, 15, 18, 19 and 23

7 Best Young Folks Game Suggestions
Nos. 11, 12, 13, 14, 20, 22 and 27

Each guest is to be supplied with a pencil and paper in order to play the thirty games suggested herein. The answers to the few games requiring them may be found in the back of the book.

1. GUGGENHEIM

Select any five letter word and then print it horizontally on the paper. If the word is "candy," write "C" (leave a fair sized space), "A" (fair sized space), "N" (fair sized space), "D" (fair sized space), "Y" (fair sized space). At the side determine your categories, for instance you might have "flowers" for the first one, "cities" for the next, "poets" for the next, etc. These are to be written, one under the other, at the left hand margin. Now it is up to everyone to fill this in. He must think of a flower beginning with "C," one beginning with "A," one beginning with "N," etc. and write its name under each of these letters. Then he must start with cities—a city beginning with "C," one beginning with "A," etc. When he has written those, he must start with poets, and so forth, depending on how many categories you selected. Of course, the winner is the one who completes his diagram first.

There is another way of playing this, and that is to give special ratings on each name guessed. If there are ten people playing and they all get "Cleveland" for a city beginning with "C," each one can score one point, but if only one person has "Cleveland" he gets ten points. In this way odd names will be thought of in order to avoid repetition and the consequent loss of scoring.

	C	A	N	D	Y
flowers		aster		daisy	
cities	cleveland	albany	Newark	Detroit	Yonkers
poets				Dante	
musical instruments	clarinet			Drum	
diseases	catarrh				

2. STOCK EXCHANGE

This game is played exactly like the box word puzzles described in Part I. Tell each guest to make 25 squares on his paper by drawing five vertical lines and five horizontal lines, evenly spaced. One person starts by naming a letter. The next person names another letter, and, as each names a particular letter, everyone must place it inside a box in such a way as to form words vertically and horizontally, just as was described in the box word games. The scoring is the same as the box word games, and the only difference is that the *guests themselves* suggest the letters, so that you never know what letter is coming, and, consequently, don't know where to place it until you hear it. If you score 35 on this game you are doing mighty well. It is one of the most entertaining games that we know of.

3. SNAP JUDGMENT

This requires a little preparation on the part of the host or hostess. Cut out as many pictures from newspapers or magazines as you wish. The more you cut out, the longer will be the game. The pictures must be of well-known people—people who are constantly in the public eye. After you have clipped these pictures from the newspapers and magazines, cut off the names and give each a number. Paste them all on a board or lay them on the floor·before your guests and let them identify the pictures. "Who is number ten?" "Who is number six?" "Number fourteen is very familiar, but I forget his name." You'll hear lots of comments and won't find many winners.

4. CONCENTRATION

Here is a chance to get your guests dizzy, but it is a lot of fun. At the word "Go!" tell them to do exactly as you instruct them to do, and read the following carefully and slowly, and do not repeat. The winner of this game deserves a worthwhile prize.

On your paper write New York.

To the right of New York write Boston.

If Chicago is not smaller than Detroit write Omaha under Boston.

If it is farther from San Francisco to Los Angeles than it is from Seattle to Chicago cross out Omaha and write Newark under New York.

If Baltimore is not larger than Philadelphia cross out Boston and write Toledo to the left of New York.

If St. Louis is north of New Orleans write Cincinnati under Omaha.

Do not cross out Toledo unless Cleveland is not in Indiana.

If Milwaukee is west of Detroit cross out New York unless Providence is larger than Bridgeport in which case cross out Omaha and write Washington over Toledo.

If Reno is not the capital of Nevada write Springfield over Boston unless you have already crossed out Boston, in which case cross out Washington and leave Cincinnati alone.

Write Atlanta under Toledo only if Toledo is in Georgia.

If you have not crossed out Cincinnati, write Denver under Toledo unless Toledo is west of Denver, in which case write Richmond to the right of Boston.

5. WORD GAME

This is an old reliable game which is the last word in simplicity. At the word "Go!" tell your guests to make as many words as they can from some fairly large word previously chosen by you. As a suggestion, you might take words like "gymnastics," "geography," "intelligence," etc. This will keep your guests busy for quite a while and, of course, the winner is the one who has the largest number of words. To make this game a little more difficult, you might rule out proper names and words of less than four letters.

6. FINISH THE STORY

This is a hilarious game which is somewhat like Endless Chain. The guests are seated in a circle. Each guest starts to write a story at the top of his paper. After he has written two or three sentences, it is up to you to cry "Stop!" and tell everyone to fold his paper and pass it to his neighbor, who must not see what was previously written. At the word "Go!" everyone continues again to write two or three sentences, trying to be as funny as possible and with the idea in mind of trying to continue the thought of the first two sentences which cannot be seen. It is not necessary for each person to continue with the story which he has already started.

This goes on until the papers have been passed completely around the circle. They are then opened and read, and believe us, you will hear some mighty funny stories.

7. NAMING TEN

This game you will find in Part III. You can make up your own categories and do not have to rely on those given in this book. Be sure that you have the answers, however, in order to avoid argument. The following are some suggestions:

Name ten countries in Europe.

Name ten western states.

Name ten musical instruments beginning with "C," etc.

8. WHO IS GUILTY?

This is a real psychological game. There is no trickery or stunt connected with it. It should work every time and is based entirely on the laws of psychology.

The object is to find the guilty person, and the guilty person is the one who has read a certain sentence which you have written.

Send two people out of the room and, after they have left, write a sentence on a piece of paper and show it to the remaining guests. Now fold this piece of paper so that it is small enough to go into the palm of the hand and call in the two people who have left the room, instructing them as follows:

"I have written a sentence on this piece of paper and am going to give it to one of you. You are both to leave the room again, but *only one* of you must read what is on that paper, the other one must not see it, and we leave you on your honor to do this. After *one* of you has read this, and the *other has not,* both of you are to return."

While the two "suspects" are out of the room make up a list of twenty words, like "red," "chair," "Bible," etc.—any words that come into your head. Included in that list must be at least *eight synonyms or words suggestive of the words which were in the sentence.* For example, if the sentence contained the word "rose," your list would contain the word "red," which would naturally bring the reaction "rose" from the one who has *not* read the paper.

When the two "suspects" return, it is up to you to put each one through a series of word reactions. As you give the first "suspect" these words, watch his reactions carefully. He must give the first word that comes into his head, *as quickly as possible!* If you say "Red," he must instantly say the first word that pops into his head. If you say "Chair," he must say the first word that pops into his head. If he reacts quickly and unselfconsciously to the entire list, you may be sure he did *not* read the sentence. If, on the other hand, he pauses or becomes nervous when he hears a word which happened to be in the sentence, you will know that he is the "guilty person."

Of course, the sentence must not be an ordinary one though it should contain simple words.

As an example, let us suggest the sentence "All cows eat grass when they get a chance." When your "Suspects" return, you will have a list, among which are included the words "bulls," "chew," "opportunity." The "suspect" who avoids saying "cow" when you say "bull," or who hesitates, is obviously the one who read the sentence. The other one will naturally say "cow." The same thing is true with the word "opportunity" which suggests the word "chance." The "guilty" one is the one who read the sentence, and your guests are the "jury."

9. TELEGRAMS

Tell your guests to write out the most appropriate telegram the initial letters of each word of which shall form a given word. To illustrate, the author gave this game over the air during a presidential campaign, and asked for a sentence, the initial letter of each word of which would spell "President." As an example he gave the following sentence: *P*erhaps *R*oosevelt *E*xpects *S*uccess *I*n *D*emocratic *E*lection *N*ext *T*uesday. One of the prize-winning replies was: *P*icture *R*epublicans *E*ating *S*pinach *I*f *D*emocrats *E*njoy *N*ational *T*urkey.

You may choose any word you wish to give your guests, but be sure that the "telegrams" which they write follow the rule and are appropriate. The funniest or most appropriate telegram wins.

10. GEOGRAPHY GAME

Hidden in the following sentences are the names of ten countries. Read them slowly to your guests and let them write down what countries they represent. As you read each statement be sure to pause and give them time to think of the country it represents and don't allow any talking or peeking on the other fellow's paper. Here they are:

1. To Fred, rowing has become a positive mania.
2. Noah wouldn't let anyone interfere with him in building his ark because he always did things in his own peculiar fashion.
3. Many large, well equipt gymnasiums have capable instructors who take you through the exercises until the gong sounds.
4. Si Perkins had to bury his neighbor's mother because the undertaker didn't show up.
5. Filthy money is burned at the mint because it is frequently full of germs.
6. After midnight the heat died down and everyone in the room had to wear a coat.

7. Harry met a girl just two weeks ago and has been calling on her every evening since.
8. Molly always drinks coffee because she simply detests tea.
9. Stanley was too timid to propose to his girl so he let Al do it for him.
10. The stein from which he drank was so gorgeous that it would go well in the home of a king!

11. CONFIDENCES

This game, old as it is, will always make a hit. Have your guests write the following at your direction:

1. Each boy writes a girl's name; each girl a boy's name. The names should be taken from among those present.
2. Now write the name of some place. Under this, write a date in the past.
3. Now write some slang expression, such as "and how" or "You're telling me," or some other expression meaning the extreme.
4. Now each boy writes a girl's name and each girl a boy's name, from among those present.
5. Put down three virtues or good qualities—exaggerate them as much as you like.
6. Put down three faults. The more slang you use, the better for this purpose.
7. Write down a number between one and one hundred.
8. Write down some word expressive of doubt, like "perhaps," "maybe," etc.

When everybody has done this, and numbered each item, read the following questions, and have each guest in turn read what is on his paper.

1. To whom did you make your first proposal? or (Who was the first man who proposed to you?)
2. Where, and when, did this happen?
3. Were you in love with one another?

4. Who else was interested in you at the time?
5. What do you consider your fiancee's best qualities?
6. What are his, or her main faults?
7. How many children do you expect to have after you are married?
8. Do you think that you will be happy?

12. DRAWING CONTEST

Let each guest write the name of some familiar animal on a sheet of paper. Now collect these sheets and scramble them in a hat. Have each guest choose one of them, and, at a given signal, start to draw on the back of the page his conception of the animal whose name appears on his paper. Have each guest number his drawing, and then collect all of them again. Now lay all the drawings on the floor and have everyone write the name of each animal and its number. The guest who has identified the most animals correctly wins the game.

13. PROFILES

Arrange the guests in a circle and have each one draw to the best of his ability the profile of the person on his right. Allow two minutes for this and then tell everyone to write the name of the person he just drew on the back of the paper and hand the paper to you.

After you have all the papers mix them up and rearrange them on the floor, face up. Now have each person try to pick out his own portrait. Needless to say there may be no winner of this game.

14. CONSEQUENCES

This is one of the oldest games that we know, and yet it is by far one of the best. In case you do not know how to play it, here are the rules:

1. Each player writes down an adjective suitable for a girl, folds the paper over, and passes it to his neighbor, who cannot see what adjective is written.

2. Each player writes the name of a girl present, folds the paper, and passes it to his neighbor.

3. Now everyone writes the word "met," and after it, an adjective descriptive of some boy present (the funnier the adjective, the better it will be). The papers are then folded, passed, and a boy's name, who is present at the party, is written down by each guest. Along with frequent foldings and passings, the guests should write "where they met," "what he said to her," "what she said to him," "what he gave her," "what she gave him," and "what everybody said about the affair."

The papers are now unfolded and each guest reads the complete story, which will be unusually funny.

15. YOU SEE BUT YOU DON'T OBSERVE

Tell your guests that you are going to mention twenty-five different articles which they see and handle every day of their lives, yet there is not one of them who can answer all the questions about these articles correctly. Of course there will be a great deal of guessing done and it is perfectly fair provided that they guess the right answer. Obviously, the winner will be the one who answers most of these questions correctly.

1. Which way does the Jack of Hearts face? ....
2. Whose head is on the 1¢ stamp? ....
3. About how long is a cigarette? ....
4. About how long is a dollar bill? ....
5. How many matches are there in an ordinary "book" of matches? ....
6. What are the dimensions of a piece of typewriting paper? ....
7. Which way do you turn a radiator handle to turn the steam on? ....
8. How many prongs has a table fork? ....
9. What is pictured on the back of a $5 bill? ....

10. How wide is a newspaper column? ....
11. What are the colors of the auto license plates in your state?
....
12. How long is the standard make of writing pencil (approx.)? ....
13. Are the cutting edges of a pair of scissors straight or slightly curved? ....
14. Is there any dark blue in a match or candle flame? ....
15. Are the divisions on your radio dial all equal? ....
16. What kind of 6 is there on a man's wrist watch? ....
17. Is the postmark used to cancel the stamp? ....
18. In your telephone dial what letters are above the 4? ....
19. Is the coin return on a pay telephone on the right side? ....
20. Approximately how far apart are the two rails in a car track? ....
21. What color stripe is directly under the blue in our flag? ......
....
22. Are the propellers in an airplane in front or in back? ....
23. How many shoelace holes are there in a man's shoe? ....
24. Approximately what is the diameter of a silver quarter?
....

16. ADVERTISING SLOGAN CONTEST

Tell your guests to write the numbers from 1 to 20 inclusive in a vertical column to the left hand edge of their papers and, as you call out an advertising slogan with its number, they must write down the product which the slogan advertises. Here are the slogans which you are to read aloud:

1. The skin you love to touch
2. Time to retire, buy ....
3. Keep that schoolgirl complexion
4. Ask the man who owns one
5. I'd walk a mile for a ....

6. Hasn't scratched yet
7. Not a cough in a carload
8. 99 and 44/100% pure
9. Good to the last drop
10. They're mild and yet they satisfy
11. No metal can touch you
12. There's a reason
13. The ham what am
14. The .... has the strength of Gibraltar
15. When better cars are built .... will build them
16. Don't envy a good complexion, use .... and have one
17. His Master's voice
18. The instrument of the immortals
19. Children cry for it
20. Where the promise is performed

17. ANAGRAMS

Tell your guests to write down the following words. They are to add to each word the letter which you give them to form a new word. The one who has the most words wins.

1. SAFE with C
2. TALE with R
3. TORE with V
4. IDEA with S
5. GORE with U
6. MASH with E
7. CRAB with E
8. FLARE with F
9. LIED with Y
10. OUST with G
11. PEST with Y
12. VEAL with G
13. BEETS with G
14. RIVET with Y
15. WIVES with L
16. RANGE with D
17. APPLE with A
18. RISEN with D
19. ANGER with T
20. OMENS with G

18. SCRAMBLES

Prepare the following list and, instead of giving the names straight, scramble up the letters in the names as indicated. You may make up any list you wish but the following is a suggestion. Answers are in the parentheses.

1. S P A N E L—The name of a city in Europe (Naples)
2. U O S H N D—The name of a river in America (Hudson)
3. L I E C H—The name of a country in South America (Chile)
4. R O G A K O N A—The name of an animal in Australia (Kangaroo)
5. E R U I T P J—The name of a planet (Jupiter)
6. R E T A S—The name of a flower (Aster)
7. P E A L P—The name of a fruit (Apple)
8. M A T O O T—The name of a vegetable (Tomato)
9. W A S P O R R—The name of a bird (Sparrow)
10. T U E L F—The name of a musical instrument (Flute)
11. L O W L E Y—The name of a color (Yellow)
12. C R U S E P—The name of a wood (Spruce)
13. R A I I D H P H T E—The name of a disease (Diphtheria)
14. V I R E N A M—The name of a Greek goddess (Minerva)
15. P E R C E—The name of a fabric (Crepe)
16. P N A I M U L T—The name of a metal (Platinum)
17. D R E A M L E—The name of a precious stone (Emerald)
18. C A T E M B H—The name of a great tragedy (Macbeth)
19. R U S E O P R I—The name of a lake in America (Superior)
20. O M E Y O E R T U D N—The name of a book in the Bible (Deuteronomy)

Give each guest a copy of the list and, at the word "Go," tell them to unscramble the words. The one who has the most correct words wins.

19. INITIALS

Before the guests arrive prepare a list of the well-known people and have as many copies of this list as there are guests. When you are ready to play this game hand each guest a list and tell them all that they are to write after each name two or three words (as the case may be) which will be most appropriate to the name and, at the same time, begin with the initials of that name. Here is an example:

1. Franklin D. Roosevelt—*Forever Defeating Republicans*
2. Robert Ripley—*Rare Realities*
3. Clark Gable—*Cinema God*
4. Mae West—*Men's Weakness*
5. Andrew Mellon—*American Millionaire*

The game can also be done with the names of the guests present if they all know one another well enough.

When everyone has finished, ask each guest in turn what he had for No. 1 and take a vote on the best answer. Do the same for No. 2 and take a vote on that. Do the same for No. 3 etc. The winner will be the one who gets the greatest number of votes. Of course the list may be as long or as short as you wish.

20. WHAT'S WRONG?

Let your guests make a thorough survey of the room. Allow five minutes for this then send them all into another room, while you make a number of alterations in the first room. Be sure that you write down these alterations so there can be no mistake. Now call your guests back, hand them each a pencil and paper and ask them to write all the changes that have taken place. Allow five minutes for this. The paper with the greatest number of correct answers wins.

21. BIOGRAPHIES

Before the guests arrive prepare a number of very short biographies of great people. Don't make these too long and don't give away too many details or you will spoil the story. Above all, don't be too vague. Here is a sample:

This genius lived in the latter half of the 18th century and the beginning of the 19th. His life was a series of disappointments but in spite of it he rose to supreme heights and became a world figure who will live forever. He never married although he was in love a number of times. He was unattractive to look at and in his youth was uncouth. In his later years he became deaf.

HIS NAME WAS ....

22. GUESSING GAME

This game requires no skill or knowledge—it is purely a matter of guessing.

Display a series of articles whose number or weight the guests must guess and record. One point is allowed for each article guessed correctly or nearly correctly, and the person who has the most points wins. Here is a suggestion for some displays:

1. The weight of a milk bottle (empty)
2. The number of pins in a small box
3. The length of a piece of string
4. The number of words on a particular page of a certain book
5. The number of pages in a closed book which anyone may select
6. The quantity of water in a kitchen pot
7. The number of cubic feet in the room
8. The number of yards in a long piece of thread
9. The weight of the host
10. The number of playing cards which you hold in your hand.

Be sure beforehand that you know the answers to all these. Be sure to weigh the empty milk bottle, count the number of pins that you place in the box, measure the length of the string, etc. You will avoid delay and argument by doing this ahead of time.

23. MUSICAL GAME

Give each guest a slip of paper with ten numbers on it in a vertical column. Have somebody who can read music and play the piano go to the piano and play ten popular selections. After each selection the guests are to write down the name of the piece after the number. The one who has the greatest number of selections named correctly, wins.

Of course, this can be done with classical music as well as popular music and if you happen to be interested in the operas of Gilbert and Sullivan it will be particularly adaptable to them. In any case it will make a most interesting game if you have a piano and a pianist.

24. WORDS, WORDS, WORDS!

Select a word of ten letters and tell each guest to write it down vertically to the left of his paper and reverse it and write it vertically to the right thus:

Suppose the word chosen is REPUBLICAN. Your guests must write it as follows:

R	N
E	A
P	C
U	I
B	L
L	B
I	U
C	P
A	E
N	R

The idea is to write the longest word you can recall beginning with R and ending with N. Then write the longest word beginning with E and ending with A. Then the longest word beginning with P and ending with C and so on all the way down the vertical word for ten letters. The result will be ten words which the guests read out. The person having the greatest number of letters in these ten words wins.

25. GENERAL QUIZ GAME

Read the following 25 questions to your guests and give them time to answer each one as you finish reading it. The winner will have the greatest number of answers correct.

1. What is the capital of Montana?
2. Who wrote Vanity Fair?
3. What is a Sepoy?
4. When was the Treaty of Versailles signed?
5. Where is Trieste?
6. Who is Westbrook Pegler?
7. Why does a glass crack when you pour boiling water into it?
8. Which is correct: "none are here" or "none is here"?
9. Where was Lincoln born?
10. Who wrote the opera Rienzi?
11. What is an analama?
12. How much is the cube of three halves?
13. What is meant by a writ of Habeas Corpus?
14. Where is Peru with respect to Argentine?
15. What is a mantilla?
16. At what temperature is water at the maximum density?
17. What is a piccolo?
18. Who won the World Series in 1936?
19. How many players are there on a Cricket team?
20. Where does chicle come from?
21. What is a G man and how did he get that name?
22. Where is the nadir?
23. Who ran against Coolidge in 1924 for the Presidency?
24. What did Lucy Stone advocate?
25. About how high is Mount Everest?

Of course you may make up as many more questions as you choose or vary this game as you see fit.

26. ADVICE

Each girl is supposed to whisper a piece of advice to a boy who writes it down. Each boy then whispers a piece of advice to a girl and she writes it down. The papers are marked "B" or "G," determining whether they are meant for a boy or a girl, and are collected. After they have been collected, they are put in a hat and redistributed, the boys taking the "G's" and the girls taking the "B's." Each one in turn reads out what is on his slip.

27. YOU SAY IT WITH TWO LETTERS

Every guest having pencil and paper, read out the following list of definitions and ask everyone to express the words which these definitions define, in two letters. For example, if you say, "not difficult," they write the two letters, EZ. If you say "the number following 79," they write down AT. The following is a list of ten words which may be used. You can make up your own if you wish, and figures may also be used:

1. devoid of, barren (MT)
2. disintegrate (DK)
3. a girl's name (KT)
4. of whatever quantity (NE)
5. prior to (B4)
6. a girl friend (QT)
7. a fabric (PK)
8. an electrical unit (OM)
9. a metal (IN)
10. to lead in a particular field (XL)

Scoring, of course, is on a percentage basis, 10% for each correct answer.

28. WORD REACTIONS

This is a real psycho-analytical game, and one which is the best of all psycho-analysis. Word reactions do give an insight to what you are thinking about, and what your complexes are. Tell your guests that you are going to give them one word and they must immediately write down on their papers a list of the first 15 words that pop into their heads. They must play fair and, in fact, they will have to play fair if you make the time limit extremely small. If you say "Barn" and count to 20 while they are writing as quickly as they can a list of 15 words, they won't have much chance to fake.

After they have all written the first 15 words that pop into their heads, have them write their names on their papers and exchange them with their neighbors. Now have each list read out and it is up to the guests to do the psycho-analysing. You have no idea what outlandish words and peculiar reactions will result!

29. QUESTION AND ANSWER

Give everybody two slips of paper, on the *first* of which each writes any question at all, afterwards writing any word at all on the *second* slip. Now collect all the questions in one bundle and all the words in another. Shuffle each bundle and then hand out to each player one question, one word paper together with a blank slip. Each player must now write on the blank slip an adequate answer to the question and in his answer he must use the word on his other paper.

30. KATE'S GAME

This is a contest having to do entirely with Kate. Read the following nine questions to your guests and have them supply the correct word:

1. What Kate is always repeating? (Duplicate)
2. What Kate is always eliminating? (Eradicate)
3. What Kate is always making speeches at ceremonials? (Dedicate)
4. What Kate makes the wheels go round? (Lubricate)
5. What Kate is full of advice? (Advocate)
6. What Kate does not go around with lowbrows? (Educate)
7. What Kate is always out of breath? (Suffocate)
8. What Kate crawls out of difficult situations? (Extricate)
9. What two Kates show the way? (Locate and Indicate)

Part VI

3O

GAMES

OF ACTION

---

7 *Best Adult Game Suggestions*
Nos. 1, 8, 10, 13, 17, 27 and 30

7 *Best Young Folks Game Suggestions*
Nos. 4, 5, 11, 15, 16, 19 and 21

1. TISSUE RACE

This is a relay race with tissue paper and tablespoons. Divide the guests into two sides and start them off as follows: A man and a girl step up to a table at one end of the room on which you have placed two drinking glasses and two tablespoons. At the word "Go" they each grab a tablespoon and run to the other end of the room or hall where you have already placed a number of pieces of tissue paper about 1½ inches square on two pillows. The idea is to pick up ONE piece of tissue paper from the pillow, carry it on the spoon to the table and put it into the glass, then return to pick up another piece, carry it on the spoon to the glass and put it in the glass, and so on until all the tissue paper that was on the pillow is put into the glass.

This is not as easy as it sounds, as tissue paper is very light and will blow off the spoon if the players run too quickly. The tissue must not be touched by anything but the spoon and if it falls off it must be picked up by the spoon. Of course, the longer the distance from the table with glasses on it to the tissue paper, the more fun it will be. The first player to put three tissue papers in the glass wins for his side and the next player starts.

Have three pieces of tissue for each player so that if there are six players on a side there will be eighteen pieces of paper on each pillow to start. After putting three pieces of tissue in the glass the first player gives his spoon to the second player who keeps up the good work and the game proceeds in regular relay fashion until one side wins.

2. CRÊPE PAPER CUTTING RACE

Before the guests arrive have a number of carefully cut strips of crêpe paper prepared. The length of these strips should be about ten feet and they should not be more than 1 inch wide. If you can't get ten foot strips then paste small strips together to make ten feet. If you can't get crêpe paper use adding machine rolls of not more than one inch wide.

Now pin all of these pieces to a cloth covered table so that one end hangs down and falls on the floor. The strips should be spaced about 2½ feet apart.

When the guests arrive and you're ready to play the game, select a man and a girl, give each a pair of scissors and let them start at the loose end and cut all the way up to the table without going off the paper. The first one who arrives at the table wins. Naturally, the narrower the paper the more difficult it will be to cut along it, and the more skill it will take to keep from going off. When the first pair of players have finished the second pair starts on two other strips. The winners of each pair play one another, and a final winner is proclaimed.

3. HOW DO YOU FEEL?

This is a new kind of feeling game. It requires a little preparation beforehand, but it is certainly worth the trouble. Before the guests arrive, procure a number of paper bags—as many bags as there will be guests. Into each bag put small pieces of the following:

A. A small chunk of bread
B. A small bit of soap
C. A small chip off a candle
D. A little piece of art gum (purchased at any art supply store)
E. A small chunk of modeling clay
F. A small piece of meat
G. A little wad of tissue paper (wet these just before you you are ready to play the game)

and as many small pieces of odds and ends as you can think up. Be sure to have things which are difficult to distinguish. The piece of soap and piece of candle, the bit of art gum and piece of stale bread, for example, are similar feeling objects.

When you are ready to play this game, give each guest a bag full of these objects. Tell them that you are going to call for this or that and they are to take it out of the bag without looking at what they are doing. If you say "Bread," they are to put their hands in the bag, feel around for the piece of bread without looking into the bag, bring it out, and show it to everyone. Anyone who brings out the wrong piece, must put it back in the bag again. The winner is the first one to have an empty bag. Of course, this game becomes easier as the bags get less full.

4. SOUP PLATE

This is more a hilarious stunt than a game, and it is sure to provide a great deal of laughter for everyone except the victim. Before your guests arrive have two soup plates half filled with water. Blacken the bottom of one soup plate by holding it over a lighted candle. After the guests arrive, call for a volunteer to play this game with you. Tell him that he must do *exactly as you do*. He must keep his eyes fixed upon you and when you smile he must smile, when you arch your eyebrows he must arch his eyebrows, etc. Give him the soup plate with the dirty bottom and keep the other soup plate in your hand. Have him stand up facing you, holding his soup plate in his left hand, just the way you do. Now tell him to watch every motion that you make and do the same, and bet him that he cannot do it. Tell him that not one man in one hundred has the observation to go through all the motions correctly.

Of course, the idea is to get him to smear his face up without knowing it, but this has to be done gradually. The first thing to do is smile—and he will smile; cough—and he will cough. Put your thumb into the water in the soup plate, take it out again and shake it—he will do the same. Put your right hand on your head for a second and take it down, and he will do the same thing. Do a number of other things and he will do the same each time. Now rub your index finger all around the bottom of your soup plate and then quickly move it across your forehead and both cheeks—he will do the same. But this time there will be considerable laughter, because his finger will be full of soot which will blacken his face without his knowing it. Of course, your face will not be blackened, since there is no soot on the bottom of *your* soup plate. If he doesn't catch on to the laughter of the crowd, you can do some other stunts and come back to this again, when he will dirty his face even more, much to the amusement of the rest.

Of course, the object of the water in the plate is so that he cannot turn it upside down. The object of having him watch you intently is so that he does not notice his dirtied finger. Don't try this on anyone who is hypersensitive or who is not willing to be a good sport. Most people will take it good naturedly.

5. THE THREAD RACE

This is to be run by two teams, each composed of a man and a girl. It is to be run in two parts, man number 1 and girl number 2 (of opposing teams) run the first part. The man has a spool of white thread and the girl a spool of black thread. The man must tie the loose end of the thread to some object like a chair leg or a door knob, etc. The girl must do the same thing. Now they must agree on a course of travel and, having agreed, they are to go as quickly as possible over this course with their spools of thread, winding (but not knotting) the thread around each object in their path. Suppose they go from the living room through the hall into the dining room, and back again to the living room where they started. As they run, they must pay out their thread, twisting it not more than once around each object they meet, but never knotting it. The number of obstacles must be the same in both cases—if the man twists his thread around five obstacles, the girl must twist her thread around some other five obstacles.

The first one back must immediately give his spool to his partner—man number 1, for example, gives his spool to girl number 1, and girl number 2 gives her spool to man number 2. This will give the man, or the girl, (as the case may be) a head start.

The object of the second part is to *wind up* the thread on the spool again. The second couple must, therefore, go over the same course carefully, winding the thread back on the spool and untwisting the thread from the obstacles without knotting or breaking it. The winner will obviously be the one who gets back to the starting point with the spool all rewound and intact. Knots are not allowed. Broken threads eliminate the racers.

When the first two teams have completed the course, the next two teams commence, and so on. The winners of each team may play one another to see who will be the final champion.

6. NEEDLE ARCHERY

Did you know that a needle with a short thread attached to it makes an excellent javelin? Try some out and see what weight needle and what length of thread goes best. Then make up your set of "javelins" by choosing as many colored threads as there are guests, and distributing one or two to each guest.

Let each guest in turn throw his "javelin" at some particular mark on the rug or carpet. This target may either be a design in the rug, or it may be drawn on a soft blanket spread over a table, making rings with chalk on the blanket. It should be in the form of a bullseye, with concentric rings, and the guests stand far enough away to make throwing reasonable. You can work up a scoring system of your own, and award a prize to the person with the highest score. Of course, this may be repeated over and over again.

7. SOUP RACE

This is a game to be played by not more than four players at one time. A little preparation is necessary in advance. All you need do is get some coloring tablets or vegetable coloring paste from your grocer's. This is the coloring used for fancy pastries and whipped cream, and you may have some in the kitchen at this moment. You need four colors: red, blue, green and yellow

—one color for each player. These are to be spaced fairly evenly around the rim of the plate, and very little is necessary in each case. If the coloring matter is in tablet form, stick it on with a little glue or paste.

When your guests arrive bring out the four plates and place them on a table. Select four players and let them choose their colors. Now carefully fill each plate with water up to a point about half an inch from the coloring. Line up the four players at a second table at the other end of the room and, at the word "GO," each player is to race for his plate, pick it up, turn around once, and take it over to the second table as quickly as he can without touching the coloring matter. The winner will be the one who first puts his plate of clear, colorless water on the second table.

Speed is not the main part of this race, as will easily be proved. The penalty for losing could be to drink a mouthful of the colored (harmless) water from the plate. If this is done be sure to use only *harmless* coloring material. This race is based on steady hands rather than long legs.

8. HORSE RACES

This game is similar to the horse race gambling game which is so popular on steamers, only it is done with living players instead of wooden horses.

Stake out your course—say from the living room wall around the dining room table, through the hall and back to the starting point. No more than six guests run at the same time; others being occupied as bookies and betting spectators. All guests not playing are allowed to bet, with the exception of the one throwing the dice and the one calling the numbers. Horses are numbered from one to six. Bets are placed before the race starts, "bookies" take in the money and give out receipts, written in their own handwriting, and marked "first race," "second race," etc. to prevent a player presenting the wrong receipt for payment. When all bets have been placed for any one race, the odds are figured and announced aloud. Everyone must bet the same amount—say five cents. The six "horses" line up at the start, one foot touching the wall, and two dice are thrown and called. Suppose number 3 and number 6 turn up; then horses number 3 and 6 take ONE STEP forward. This step may be as long as they like, provided it is *just one step*. (It is true that certain "horses" can take larger strides than others, but, since these will probably have more money bet upon them or more bets on them, the odds will be lower than on the other "horses"). From now on, the game proceeds just like a horse race on the steamers.

Each time the dice are thrown the corresponding numbered horses move one step forward. Horses are not allowed to block one another in their movements. When doubles are thrown, the horse gets two steps instead of one. Of course, the winner is the one who gets back to the starting point first. At this time, the bets are paid off and a new race starts with six other guests.

9. THE HAT GAME

This game is played with a man's hat and a pack of playing cards. The hat is turned upside down and placed on the floor of the room against one wall. Each player stands about ten feet away and tries to toss cards into the hat. If you think this is easy, just try it. Out of 52 cards it is doubtful if you can throw 15 into the hat. It is lots of fun, and, as far as we know, may require skill. This game lends itself to a number of different methods of scoring. For example, you can either go by the number of cards in the hat at a given distance, or you can go by the face value of the cards. If you throw in the ace of spades you might get ten points, where the two of clubs would only count one point. Make up your own system on this before your guests arrive.

10. A NUTTY GAME

Divide your guests into two groups and seat them in two rows of chairs facing each other. At each end of each row, place a bowl. The first man in each row has a bowl beside him and in the bowl there are a dozen walnuts. At the word "GO" these two men begin "feeding" their respective sides with nuts. The nuts must pass from each player to his neighbor, one at a time, and as each nut reaches the other end of the line it is placed in an empty bowl. As soon as the 12th nut reaches the bowl at the other end of either line, the person at that end begins to return them in the same manner. The side which empties the first bowl and refills it again, wins.

Nuts must be passed one at a time and must pass through each player's hands in turn. If a player drops a nut, he must pick it up before he passes the next nut to his neighbor. The nuts must go from a full bowl at one end of the line to an empty bowl at the other, and back again to the original bowl, in the shortest possible time. Another way to play this game is not to start the second nut going until the first nut reaches the empty bowl at the other end of the line. As soon as the last player drops this nut in the bowl, the first player starts the second nut going, etc.

11. BLIND SWAT

This is a real rough-house game, in which two boys take part. Give each one a rolled-up newspaper in the form of a club. Now blindfold both of them and tell them to hold hands (left hands only). They are not to let go under any circumstances.

While these two boys are thus blindfolded, they are to take the rolled-up newspapers in their right hands and hit one another with them. This will not be easy, since they are blindfolded and are holding hands—but it will be a lot of fun to watch. The score keeper will keep track of the number of hits scored, a time limit set, and, of course, the winner proclaimed. You had better remove all breakable objects before starting.

[182]

12. THE KANGAROO

Lay out four rows of thin, light sticks. Place the sticks about three feet apart and have as many as the room will permit. Select a player for each row, and, at the word "GO," all players must start to hop on one foot over each stick until they arrive at the last stick. As soon as a player arrives at the last stick, he turns around, still on one foot, and starts back, only this time after he hops over each stick, he must stoop down and pick it up. If he drops a stick he must immediately start all over again. If he loses his balance and stands on both feet he must also start over again. The winner will be the one who is the first to bring back all the sticks in his row.

13. SMILE

All the girls in the room are to face the men and try to make them smile or laugh. The girls may laugh, tell funny stories or do anything else they choose to get the men to "thaw out" and look cheerful. Naturally the men try hard not to laugh or smile and if any man is so "unmanly" as to give in and laugh or smile he immediately joins the girls and tries to get his fellow men to do the same. The surprise comes at the end of the game when only one or two men are left. These serious glum creatures think that they are going to win a prize or win the game while as a matter of fact they are each fined 10¢ for being the biggest kill-joys at the party!

14. STORK'S NINEPINS

Select nine players to stand at one end of the room on one foot only. It makes no difference which foot and it doesn't matter if they change from one foot to the other every once in a while, but they must be on one foot all the time. Now choose three girls to be the bowlers and give each girl in turn a large ball (medicine or basket ball) and tell her to roll it between these human ninepins. As the ball nears them they will naturally feel quite uncomfortable and the chances are that some of them will either stand on both feet or lose their balance and fall over. In either case they will be disqualified. The one holding out the longest wins the game. Of course the girls take turns in rolling the ball.

15. NUMBER PLEASE

Choose sides and line up each side facing the other. Give each guest a number (which you may either pin on his coat or hang around his or her neck) and tell him that that is his official number. Side A has its numbers (from 1 to 9 including 0) and side B has the same. A judge is chosen to stand at one end of the room and pick numbers from a hat. Suppose he picks 365. He calls out "Side A—number 365" at this instant number 3, number 6 and number 5 rush out and form this number as quickly as possible. If they form 563, 635, 356 or any other combination but 365 they are sent back and side B is given a chance. This is done 10 times for each side and the side that gets the greatest number of correct numbers wins. In case you have more than ten on each side use duplicates, for example 1831, 6486, etc.

Of course the numbers that you put into the hat will have no duplicates unless the players have duplicates. The numbers in the hat should all be between 100 and 10,000 and should never have any two digits alike unless more than ten players on each side are playing.

16. OBSTACLE RACE

Select two people and tell them that they must walk, blindfolded, from one end of the room to the other without bumping into a number of obstacles which you will put in their way. These obstacles may be anything in the room such as chairs, stools, lamps, etc. Tell them to take a good look at the layout of the room before you blindfold them so that they will be able to know about where each obstacle is.

Now blindfold them and, while you are doing it have someone remove *all* obstacles in the room so that the two players will have clear sailing. Of course they don't know this and when they start out on the "race" they will proceed with unusual care and walk so foolishly through nothing at all that everyone will laugh. After a while remove the blindfold and let them see how foolish they were!

17. THAT'S RIGHT, YOU'RE WRONG!

This game requires plenty of wits and quick thinking.

All the girls stand up in a line and face the boys who are also standing in another line about four feet away. Someone is selected as a royal inquisitor who must ask questions. He stands at the head of both lines half way between them and starts by asking the first boy a question which the girl opposite must answer *falsely*. For example he might say "How old are you," to the boy. The boy remains silent while the girl opposite quickly says 73! He then turns to the girl and asks her a question which the boy opposite her (next to the first boy) must answer *truthfully*. For example he might say "What color hair have you?" and the second boy in line will quickly say "brown" while the girl says nothing.

The idea is for the girls to answer falsely and the boys to answer truthfully. *The person questioned never answers*—it is always the one opposite and next in line who answers. Anyone disobeying these rules is out and must step one pace behind and be out of the game. The winner is the one who can hold out the longest.

18. SO NEAR AND YET SO FAR!

The idea of this game is to walk across the room blindfolded while holding hands with another blindfolded person. It is anything but easy to do and looks so foolish when you get three couples doing it at the same time that it is sure to produce a great deal of laughter.

Blindfold three couples who must keep holding hands and

not let go. At the word "GO" let them try to find their way to the goal at the other end of the room. They must not let go of one another or they will be disqualified. The couple reaching the goal first, of course, wins.

19. TUMBLE-TUSSLE

This is a parlor wrestling match played by two boys (two girls may play too if they are game) and sure to bring plenty of laughs to the rest of the crowd!

Each boy is seated on the floor with his back to the other. His knees are bent up and his hands are clasped under his knees. While in this position his wrists are tied with a handkerchief and his two feet are also tied with another handkerchief. Both boys are now quite helpless with their backs to one another. It is now up to one of them to knock the other over. To watch these two helpless boys try to "get one another down" is really extremely funny. Of course the winner will be the one who succeeds in knocking the other one over. This can be done in pairs and the final winners fight it out for the championship.

20. SCISSORS GAME

Here is an old favorite which is always dependable. Arrange your guests in a circle and give one of them a pair of scissors. Tell him to pass the scissors to his neighbor saying the following:

"I receive this crossed and pass it uncrossed" as the case may be.

Of course the scissors will be open or shut, depending upon how each person passes it to his neighbor. Naturally everyone thinks that if it is open it is crossed and if shut it is uncrossed. If Mr. Jones receives it open and passes it shut he will naturally say "I receive this crossed and pass it uncrossed" but that may not be the case. It all depends on whether or not he has his *legs crossed*—for the *legs* are the clue and not the scissors. Everytime someone makes an error it is up to you to say "that is not so" and correct him. When it comes to your turn you can either cross your legs or uncross them and you will be saying what is so, much to the amazement of the guests. You would be surprised how few people will catch on to the clue. Keep it up until someone discovers that it has nothing to do with the scissors but has entirely to do with the person's legs being crossed or uncrossed.

21. BUBBLE RACE

This is a sort of basketball with a bubble. Two sides are chosen and bubble pipes and soapy water provided each side. Each side must have a bubble blower, a fanner and a goal man. The two fanners stand facing one another in the center of the room. Each has a piece of cardboard or a fan in his hand. At the word "GO" the bubble blower for side A blows a bubble and the two fanners try to fan this bubble over toward their respective goals. If the bubble bursts, the two fanners start over again at the point where the bubble has burst, the other bubble blower blowing the next bubble. The object is to get the bubble over the goal line.

22. SIMON SAYS:

Divide your guests into two sides who sit opposite each other at a table. The object of this game is for one side to conceal a dime (which is moving among the players of one team) from the other side.

Start the game by tossing the coin to see which side shall have charge of the dime first. When this has been done a captain of the offensive team is selected and whatever he says goes. If any other member of the team gives a command and anyone on the opposing team obeys it, the coin is forfeited and the other side gets it.

Now suppose team A has the coin. The captain of team B

says, as his first command "UP SIMON" whereupon everyone on team A puts his hands high in the air (fists closed of course, so that nobody will be able to see where the dime is).

The next command by captain B is "DOWN SIMON" whereupon all the players on team A place their hands under the table and may pass the dime from hand to hand if they wish. The next order is "ON THE TABLE SIMON" whereupon all hands must be slapped palms down on the table (be careful not to rattle the coin when you do this as it will give the whole thing away).

Captain B now has to locate the dime. He can either guess directly or work by the process of elimination. If he guesses directly and pointing to one particular hand says "it's under there!" he scores 5 points if he is right and the other side scores 5 points if he is wrong. Whichever side scores has the custody of the coin for the next time.

If captain B succeeds in eliminating all the players and finding the coin in the last player's hand then his side scores 5 points; if not, the opposing side scores 5 points. The game is 50 points.

One last word—remember that any member of the attacking team (team B in this case) may give a command to the other side but only the captain is to be obeyed.

23. RELAY RACES

This game is played with two highball glasses, two ice cubes and two bread boards. The players are lined up in two parallel rows, the same number in each row, to form two opposing teams.

Player No. 1 of each team starts with an ice cube in his glass and player No. 2 of each team holds the bread board flat on the palms of his hands, ready to "receive" the ice cube. At the word "GO" players No. 1 of each team pour their cubes onto the bread board held by players No. 2. The boards are then passed to the next players of each team as quickly as possible without "spilling" the ice cube and so on all the way down the line and ack again to No. 1 where it is returned to the highball glass. The game is very much like No. 10—"A NUTTY GAME" only it is played with ice cubes instead of walnuts.

24. BASEBALL

This entirely new game by Gerald Kaufman is sure to prove a winner for everyone who likes baseball. It is played with a marble on a bridge table and the properties are very simple. They are:

1 marble
2 strips of cardboard 2 inches wide and a foot long
3 cardboard bases about 1 inch square, pinned in their proper places at 1st, 2nd and 3rd base on the table
1 pencil and pad
As many teaspoons as there are players

There must be a pitcher, a batter and as many fielders as you choose, each fielder having a teaspoon. The more fielders there are the more they will get in one another's way and so help the opposing team. It is best to have four on each side; a pitcher, a batter and two fielders.

The pitcher starts by letting the marble roll down his cardboard chute toward the batter who must receive this marble and, without taking his cardboard chute off the table, roll the marble in any direction he chooses. As soon as the marble leaves the batter he must grab the pad and pencil and write FIRST BASE as fast as he can. In the meantime the fielders are catching the marble with their spoons (they must catch it as it leaves the table and not scoop it up off the table). The first thing that a fielder must do when he has caught the marble is to touch the batter out at first—or at the base to which he is "running." He does this by carrying the spoon with the marble in it over to the base and touching that base. He must do this before the batter writes his base. If he does, the batter is OUT; if he doesn't the batter is SAFE. The game is otherwise played just like One-o-cat and there are no such things as strikes or balls or fouls.

The name of the NEXT base to which you are going is always written on the pad. If you happen to be on first and you try to go to second after your teammate has just rolled the ball, you must both write on the pad. You write SECOND BASE and he writes FIRST BASE.

25. I KNOW YOU

Blindfold half of your guests and arrange the chairs so that each blindfolded person will sit next to an empty chair. Now let the other half (those who are not blindfolded) sit in these vacant chairs so that each blindfolded person will sit next to one who is not blindfolded.

Now, starting with the first "couple," have the player who is not blindfolded sing a short song in a disguised voice. When he has finished it is up to his blindfolded neighbor to call him by name. If he does this correctly he may remove his blindfold, if not he must keep it on. In either case the next "couple" gets a chance and this keeps on until everyone has sung and guessed.

After each song and subsequent guess, the unblindfolded players get up and move around and exchange seats with one another. The last one to have his bandage removed gets the booby prize!

26. SPOONING CONTEST

This is a good game to play when the refreshments are served. Tie two teaspoons together with twine so that they are about 18 inches apart and pair off the guests so that a girl has one spoon and a boy has the other. At the word "GO" they are all to start eating the ice cream (which will not be so easy to do) and the first couple who finishes wins and is entitled to eat the next portion without any strings to it.

27. GET RID OF THE ORANGE

Arrange two circles, the girls on the inside and the boys on the outside. Give one of the boys an orange and one of the girls an ice cube and start things going. Both the orange and the ice cube are to be passed from one to the other—the orange going around the boy's circle and the ice going around the girl's circle. Now, as soon as you clap your hands or shout "STOP" the boy who happens to have the orange must buy the girl who happens to hold the ice cube a box of candy.

Of course the boys will try to get rid of the orange as quickly as they can while the girls will hold on to the ice cube as long as they are able (which will not be long). The boys must pass the orange in one direction while the girls pass the ice cube in the opposite direction.

28. FOLDING CHAIR RELAY RACE

This game is a whale of a lot of fun to do. Divide your guests into two teams with the same number of boys and girls on each team.

On the floor at one end of the room or hallway have two folded bridge chairs about four feet apart. The players are at the other end of the room and at the word "GO" the first couple of each team runs over to the chairs, the boys open them as quickly as they can and the girls sit down in them and count to ten rapidly. The girls then get up and the boys fold up the chairs as quickly as they can and leave them where they found them. These two couples then run back to the next two couples who are "rarin' to go" and the same thing takes place all over again. The team who finishes first wins the race.

29. PING PONG FOOTBALL

Divide the dining room table into four equal parts with the aid of a piece of chalk. Now pick two teams with a boy and a girl on each team and arrange them as shown in the diagram:

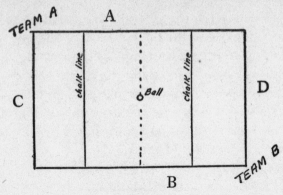

Each player now has his particular area to take care of and must act only when the ball comes inside that area. The ball (a ping-pong ball) is now placed in the center of the table and at the word "GO" players A and B start blowing the ball toward the opposite ends of the table, A's goal being one end and B's goal being the other end similar to a football field. As soon as the ball crosses the middle section into one of the end quarters it is up to player C or player D to blow it back again. The object of the game is to blow the ball off the table at one of the ends and make a "Blowdown." The team scoring the greatest number of "Blowdowns" in twenty minutes wins.

30. WHISTLE-CRACKER

Line up the guests in two parallel rows, the boys in one row and the girls in the other. Now give each guest a cracker which must not be eaten until the time comes. At the word "GO" the first boy and the first girl start to eat their crackers and as soon as they have finished they must whistle clearly, turn around and face the person behind who must immediately start to eat his cracker, finish it, whistle clearly, turn around and face the person behind him and so on all the way down the line. The first line to finish wins.

Part VII

GAMES FOR
SPECIAL OCCASIONS

SUGGESTIONS FOR DRESS-UP PARTIES

(Award a Prize in Each Case for the Best or Funniest Costume)

1. FANCY DRESS FROM THE NECK UP; evening dress from the neck down. The face must be covered and the masks or headgear must be in ridiculous contrast to the evening dress, for example: A giraffe's head on a tuxedo or a sunflower head on an evening dress.

2. HOBO PARTY where the men come as bums and hoboes. Have them wear their oldest clothes and not shave for a day or so, for the worse they look the better. The girls shouldn't fix their hair and should be in keeping with the appearance of the men. Welcome all guests at the back door and as they come in hand them a paper bag with a sandwich in it—just to give a little realism to the scene.

3. MIXED UP PARTY where the men come dressed as girls and the girls come dressed as men. This will produce one of the funniest appearances you have ever seen.

4. SUPPRESSED DESIRE PARTY where each guest comes as his own particular suppressed desire. Whatever your desire is, try to picture it and come dressed as it.

5. SHIPWRECK PARTY where each guest comes dressed as he would if he were in a shipwreck late at night. The more hurriedly dressed they are, the better it will be.

6. CHILDREN'S PARTY where each guest comes as a little child or even a baby.

7. CHARACTER PARTY where each guest comes as a famous character in fiction or history.

8. IMPROVISED COSTUME PARTY where each guest is given a newspaper, a scissors and a box of pins and told to make his or her own costume. Some crazy costumes will be worn—especially by the men.

[195]

9. BACKWARDS PARTY where everyone dresses with front to the back and the back to the front. The guests come to the back door, walk in backwards and, instead of greeting the host and hostess they thank them and tell them what a fine time they had. When they leave they say "Hello." If you serve sandwiches and ice cream, serve the ice cream first. Remember to do EVERYTHING backwards.

LINCOLN'S BIRTHDAY

(*Gettysburg Address*)

When you are ready to play this game give each guest a pencil and paper; tell them that you are going to read the Lincoln Gettysburg Address to them but unfortunately it will not be entirely complete. Every once in a while you will pause and they are to write down the missing word or words. You will tell them how many words are missing and as soon as they have written them down you will continue reading. The winner will be the one who has the greatest number of correct words on his paper.

Now slowly read the following, pausing at each blank to allow the guests to write in the missing word. In the second paragraph there are six words missing after the "Now we are . . ." Be sure to tell everyone that six words are missing before continuing with "testing whether that nation . . ."

This will be a lot of fun to do, and you will be surprised how few people really know this famous masterpiece word for word.

Fourscore and seven years ago our fathers brought forth —— this continent a new nation, conceived in ———— and dedicated to the proposition that all men are created equal.

Now we are —— —— —— —— —— ——, testing whether that nation or any nation so conceived and so dedicated can —— ——. We are —— —— —— —— —— of that ——. We have come to dedicate a portion of that —— as a —— —— —— of those who —— —— —— —— that that nation —— ——. It is altogether fitting and proper that we should do this.

But, —— —— —— ——, we cannot dedicate, we cannot ——, we cannot —— —— ——. The brave men, living and dead, —— —— ——, have —— it, far above our —— —— to add or ——. The world will little note, nor long remember, what we say here, but it can never forget what —— —— ——. It is for us the living, rather, —— —— —— —— to the —— —— which —— —— —— —— have thus —— —— —— ——. It is rather for us to —— —— —— —— the great task remaining before us—that from —— —— —— —— —— —— —— —— —— —— —— which they gave the last —— —— —— —— that we here —— —— that these dead shall not have died in vain—that this nation, under God, shall have a new birth of freedom—and that government of the people, by the people, for the people shall not perish from the earth.

WASHINGTON'S BIRTHDAY

(*Washington Crossing the Delaware*)

It is well known that when Washington crossed the Delaware he didn't have an easy time of it because of the large pieces of floating ice which hit against his small row boat.

In honor of George, let one person at a time try to cross the room on paper icebergs in the following manner:

Place sheets of typewriter paper about 2 feet apart in a zig-zag fashion from one end of the room to the other end. Number these sheets. Now call for a Washington and when he volunteers, tie his ankles together and start him on paper number 1. He is to hop from paper 1 to paper 2 then to 3, 4, 5, etc. until he reaches the other end of the room. He may be able to do it all right but it is also a question of speed and it is up to you to time him and record it. When he is finished the next volunteer tries and the one who crosses in the shortest time wins.

Be sure not to make it too difficult: don't have the papers too far apart and make the numbers on them clear and legible. You may place them anywhere you like and cover the entire room with them, just as long as they lead from one end of the room to the other and they are not too close together.

Truth

In honor of Washington the old game of truth is particularly appropriate. This game is a lot of fun with a crowd who is willing to be good sports and not take offense. If you have any sensitive people at the party we advise you not to play this.

Make a list of characteristics at the left hand edge of a piece of paper and the names of each person at the party above as indicated in the diagram. As soon as this is done choose someone to rate and send him out of the room with instructions to rate himself exactly as he sees himself. He must tell the truth. When he has gone have everyone in the room rate him truthfully. Rating is done on a basis of ten.

Now call in the person who went out and have him read his opinion of himself to the crowd while you collect all papers and average up each item to strike a general average. When he is finished with his own rating, read your combined and average rating of him and see what the various differences are.

	Self appeal	Brains	Beauty	Sincerity	Originality	Sense of Humor
Flo	6	7	4	9	2	4
Jack	3	9	1	10	5	7
May	9	1	9	9	0	2
Jerry	6	7	4	9	5	9
Kitty	8	7	8	10	7	9
Emily	4	8	4	9	3	6

ST. VALENTINE'S DAY

Heart Throbs

There are very few parties where one of the boys is not interested in one of the girls. As a rule everyone knows who John's girl friend is and whom Mary is crazy about.

Select a boy and a girl who are known to be sort of . . . well, you know . . . and have them sit facing one another. Now let each one hold the other's pulse and count the heart beats aloud without smiling or blinking or looking anywhere except into each other's eyes. Everyone else may laugh and talk as much as he wants but the valentine couple must be absolutely serious while they look into one another's eyes, feel each other's pulses and count out loud for two minutes.

If the valentine couple succeeds in doing their stunt you may be sure that they are pretty far gone on one another; if not, it's just a mild crush and nothing more.

Limericks

Make up Limericks for each of your guests and let them fill in the last line. This is much easier than it sounds and, with a little practice beforehand you will be able to do it very well. As you know a limerick must follow certain rules in regard to meter and rhyme and if you examine the following Limerick you will see what we mean:

There was a young man who said "why
Can't I look through my ear with my eye?
      If I put my mind to it
      I'm sure I could do it
You never can tell till you try."

The first two lines and the last line rhyme. The 3rd and 4th lines are much shorter and rhyme.

You can begin all your Limericks with

There was a young man (lady) named ....

and place the name of boy or girl in the blank.

Who loved a young lady (fellow) named............................

and place the name of the girl or the boy in the blank making sure that it rhymes with the first name. Now all you need do is write two short lines which rhyme and are funny and let one of your guests fill out the last line. Here is a typical Limerick, as-

[200]

suming that there is a Jesse and a Bessie among your guests:

> There was a young lady named *Bessie*
> Who's sweet on a fellow named *Jesse*
>> It's easy to know
>> That wherever they go

....

If you don't happen to have couples who rhyme you can use your ingenuity and rhyme a name with some other word, Harry, for example will rhyme with marry, Flora with adore her, Bert with flirt, etc.

Now make up as many different limericks as there are people at your party (one for each) and leave the last line out. When the guests arrive give each one a limerick and have them all fill out the last line. The best and funniest line wins.

ST. PATRICK'S DAY

Bubble Blowing Contest

Supply each guest with a clay pipe tied with a green ribbon. Now produce a big bowl of soapy water and have each guest in turn come up and blow as large a bubble as he can, making a careful note of the winner. Now start over again and have each guest blow as small a bubble as he can and note the winner. The next is the highest bubble, then the most bubbles from one wetting of the pipe. The winners of each of these contests now compete in the finals and the winner of that is awarded a prize appropriate for St. Patrick's day.

Kissing the Blarney Stone

Before the guests arrive prepare two flattering letters; one to one of the girls who is going to be at the party, and the other to one of the boys who will be there. These letters should be typewritten, if possible, and in case you want to save time thinking up what to say, you may copy the following two letters:

DEAR HELEN (or any other girl's name you choose)
I have the utmost respect and the highest admiration for your great intellect and unusual culture. You are one of the few girls who combines brilliant and sparkling wit with dignity and self possession! Your attractive appearance is exceeded only by your remarkable personality. What is this fascination that you have over men that draws them to you in dozen lots like a magnet attracts carpet tacks? I have never seen anyone so beautiful and charming in my life for verily you have the mind of an Einstein behind the face of a Venus!

DEAR FRED (or any other boy's name you choose)
It is an honor to know you and to be considered one of your friends. Your marvelous physique, your manly strength and strikingly handsome face, coupled with your great wisdom and dazzling mind sets my heart a-twitter when I am in your presence. You are model manhood personified—and I am only a mere girl who worships you like a god! What is the secret of your great success in life? What is this magnetism that you hold over all of womankind? How, at your early years did you acquire such a fund of knowledge and wisdom and why are you so extremely modest about it all? Perhaps it is because you rank with the world's outstanding men!

When the guests arrive, have a large flat piece of marble or slate on the table and call for a volunteer to "kiss the Blarney Stone." Call first for a boy and when he volunteers tell him that the old custom is to write his name while he is kissing the Blarney Stone. As soon as he bends over to kiss the stone, give him a pencil and tell him he must write his name without looking up while he is kissing the stone. He will do this, much to the amusement of the rest of the crowd. Of course you must substitute the letter which you wrote to the girl, folded in such a way as not to show any typing—it is to look like a blank piece of paper. What the boy really is doing is signing the letter, but he doesn't know it.

When the boy has finished kissing the Blarney Stone and writing his name, call for a girl to do the same thing. Of course there should be a lot of joking and kidding around to take everybody's mind off the real issue—the letters. The girl must do the same thing—she must write her name too, only this time you substitute the letter which you wrote to the boy.

Now, say nothing more about this and pretend that it is all over. Play some other game, but be sure to disappear, without anyone seeing you, sometime before refreshments are served and place the girl's letter in her place at the table and the boy's letter at his place at the table.

Imagine the surprise when both the girl and the boy sit down to the table and see these two ridiculously flattering letters signed by the two who kissed the Blarney Stone.

FOURTH OF JULY

The Star Spangled Banner

How many Americans know all the words to the three stanzas of the *Star Spangled Banner?* The answer is very few, and because of this fact you can play an interesting game by having everyone stand up while you conduct the National Anthem. Of course you will have the words in front of you while you are leading your guests in song, but it is up to you, as soon as you see or hear anyone miss the lines, to make him about face—turn his back to you.

The first stanza will be easy, since everyone knows it, but when you come to the second and third stanzas you will have to watch everyone carefully and be sure to have them turn their backs to you as soon as they make a mistake or stop singing the words.

The one who lasts the longest is the winner, but you may be pretty sure that before you finish the three stanzas everyone will have turned an about face.

Flag Coloring

Give each guest a pencil and paper and tell him to make a list of numbers from one to ten. The problem is to write after each number the colors in that particular flag, for instance, if you say "One. What are the colors in the American Flag"? the obvious

answer is, "Red, White and Blue." But that is too easy, so try
the following:

1. British Flag
2. French Flag
3. Italian Flag
4. The Flag of the Irish Free State
5. The Chinese Flag
6. The Japanese Flag
7. The Swiss Flag
8. The Greek Flag
9. The Flag of Brazil
10. The Mexican Flag

HALLOWE'EN

A Number of Old Stunts and Games

Perhaps Hallowe'en Parties are the most popular of all because Hallowe'en has a definite tie-up with spooks and pranks
and tricks. We will include in this paragraph a general review
of the various things that are done on Hallowe'en. These are by
no means new, yet we are suggesting them just as a sort of résumé
of what has been done.

Your Fortune

Five soup plates are put next to one another on a table. The
first one contains clear water, the second one soapy water, the
third one a ring, the fourth one a little earth or talcum powder,
and the fifth one nothing at all. Each guest is blindfolded and
led to the table, where he must dip his finger into one of the
soup plates. The contents of these plates mean the following:

Clear water means a happy marriage within the next five
years,

Soapy water means an unhappy marriage within the next
five years,

The ring means a proposal within the next three weeks,

The earth means a long journey within a month,

The empty soup plate denotes a marriageless, empty life.

Stunts on Hallowe'en

The old stunt of ducking for floating apples in a big pan of water and trying to find a hidden penny with your mouth in a big dish of flour are well known and are always fun to do. Then there is the apple seed trick where the girl names five apple seeds after boys at the party. She wets these seeds and places them on her forehead. The first seed that falls off is the boy who is going to propose to her. There is also the mirror stunt which is to be played in a dark room with a candle. A girl approaches a medium-sized mirror (which is hung on a wall) with a lighted candle. The candle is the only light in the room and guests are standing all around. The first boy's face that the girl sees in the mirror will be her future husband. This can also be done with boys for their future wives.

There are any number of stunts and tricks which are played over and over again on Hallowe'en, most of which you undoubtedly know. They all have to do with fortune telling, crystal gazing or ghosts and spooks. In the following paragraph we give a new and original stunt which is sure to bring a thrill to your Hallowe'en Party.

The Ghost's Return

This is a grand trick and will give your guests the creeps. Have a dark seance with not more than 6 people seated around a light table—preferably a bridge table. The only light in the room must be centered on the table so that nobody cheats. The host is the medium and asks the spirits the questions. The spirits will answer through the table. If it tips once it means "YES" and if it tips twice it means "NO."

Now everyone is seated around the table and all hands must be placed flat on the table so the little finger of one hand is in contact with the thumb of the next hand. This will "complete the circuit." To add to all this, have everyone touch knees under the table—also "to complete the circuit." Now ask one of the people to get up and turn out the high lights and leave only the bridge lamp lit and near the table so that everyone can see that there is no trickery. As soon as this is done and the person who put the lights out returns to the table, the séance begins. The table will mysteriously tip once for YES and twice for NO after each question much to the horror of the guests!

How is it done? Very simple. The person who turns out the lights is in on the trick. He must be a man and must have a foot rule concealed in his right sleeve. As soon as he comes back and takes his place at the table, he allows the ruler to project out a little and catch UNDERNEATH the table while his hand is innocently above the table. His sleeve is now the connecting link between his wrist and the ruler and if he moves his wrist he will tip the table easily without anyone knowing. This he does after every question. The illustration shows how this can be done.

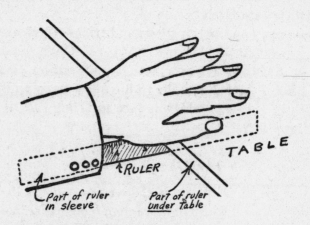

Part of ruler
in sleeve ⌐RULER Part of ruler
under table

IF ARM IS MOVED UP SLIGHTLY —
the ruler, pressing against the bottom of the
table, will cause Table to Tilt slightly.

Part VIII

20
MAGIC TRICKS

13
STUNTS

CRAZY BETS

---

1. MAGIC WATER COLORS

Get four colored pencils and let someone in on this trick because it is a swell one. Show these four colored pencils to your confederate without your guests knowing anything about it, and tell him that No. 1 stands for RED, No. 2 stands for WHITE, No. 3 stands for BLUE and No. 4 stands for GREEN. This is very easy to remember: RED, WHITE, BLUE, GREEN— 1, 2, 3, 4.

Tell your confederate that you are going to send him a soup plate full of water and he is to feel underneath the plate near the center for little blobs of chewing gum. The number of blobs determine the "color of the water." Now tell him what is going to take place. He is to hide in another room while the guests choose a colored pencil. You are going to dip the chosen colored pencil into the water in the soup plate and hand the soup plate to someone to take out to him. He is to holler out (so everyone can hear) what colored pencil was dipped into the water in the soup plate. He is to say that he sees the water colored that color. Of course as he holds the plate and peers into the water, he must scrape all the blobs of chewing gum from under the plate so that nobody will catch on to the trick.

Of course it is up to you to have the plate prepared with 4 blobs of chewing gum underneath it before you start. When you show it to your guests YOU are holding it and if you choose the RED pencil all you need do is scrape off three of the blobs (leaving 1 for RED) and dispose of these blobs without anyone seeing you do it. If you chose BLUE you would scrape off only one blob (leaving 3 for BLUE). When you give the plate to one of your guests to take inside to your confederate be sure that he holds the plate with *both hands* so he has no chance of feeling underneath the plate. Have the plate quite full of water.

Do not try to repeat this trick immediately. Later on when you or your confederate can slip out unnoticed, one of you can prepare the plate all over again.

2. MAGIC FIRE COLORS

This is essentially the same trick as above. The code is just the same but the trick is done with colored paper which is burned up and carried inside on a piece of plain paper. The same confederate goes in the other room and the guests choose one of four colored papers. Suppose they choose GREEN. You now take the green paper, light it and allow the ashes to fall on the slip of plain white paper which you hold in your hand. You now hand these ashes on this paper to someone and tell him to carry it carefully on the *palm of his hand* into the room where your partner is and he will tell the color of the paper that was burned!

The code is still very simple. Instead of chewing gum blobs underneath a soup plate, you make thumb nail marks on the paper which contains the ashes. In the case of GREEN you make 4 tiny thumb nail marks which your confederate looks for while he is "peering into the ashes" on the paper.

Be sure that the thumb nail marks are not obvious and when you make them do it without being observed. Tell your confederate to scramble up the paper when he names the color so nobody will have a chance to examine it. You can do this trick as often as you like.

3. AN AMAZING PSYCHIC TRICK

This trick is one of the most baffling in all magic. Nobody will ever catch on to it and it will mystify everybody completely! It should be done by a man and wife or brother and sister or two people who live together and can practice a little, though it is very simple. Here it is in its simplest form:

Girl leaves the room and someone takes a card and shows it to everyone in the room. The card is put back into the pack and the pack is shuffled thoroughly and put on a table face down. Girl comes in and guesses the card!

Suppose the 8 of Spades were chosen. It is put back into the pack and the pack is shuffled and put on the table. The girl enters and says:

"It's a black card"	You say "Yeh"
"It's a Spade"	You don't say anything.
"It is the 8 of Spades!"	

This certainly seems unexplainable to everyone but it is extremely simple when you know how. Here is the clue:

The four edges of the table represent the four suits. Looking down at the table the upper edge is Spades, the right edge Hearts, the lower edge Diamonds and the left edge Clubs. Of course the pack need not be placed way over at the edge but it MUST be placed enough off center to indicate the suit. In this case the pack is carelessly put over toward the "far" edge or the "top" of the table.

From now on it is just a question of memorizing 4 very simple things given the following chart:

	YES	YEH	YEP	NO ANSWER
YES	Ace	2	3	or 4
YEH............	5	6	7	or 8
YEP	9	10	J	or Q
No answer at all to any question .... King				

From this table you can see that YES means one of four cards: Ace, 2, 3 and 4, so if you answer YES the girl knows it is one of these cards. Your next answer will give the card since, if you look at each column you will see YES, YEH, YEP and NO ANSWER just as before. The 10, for example is YEP-YEH, the 5 is YEH-YES.

Now practice a little and see why these cards are what we say they are:

3 is YES-YEP

8 is YEH-NO ANSWER

4 is YES-NO ANSWER

2 is YES-YEH

NO ANSWER AT ALL TO ANYTHING .... KING

As soon as the girl sees the position of the pack on the table she knows the suit. She then says:

"It's a black card" (this gives you a chance to say YES, YEH, YEP or NOTHING AT ALL)

you say YEH

"It's a Spade" (this gives you a chance for the second YES, YEH, YEP or SILENCE)

you say NOTHING

The girl knows that YEH-NO ANSWER is 8. She knew the suit as soon as she saw the table so she says:

"The 8 of Spades"

One more example: Suppose the 3 of diamonds is picked.

The cards are put toward the BOTTOM or *near edge* of the table as you face it. You know then that it is a diamond. You then say:

"It's a red card" and your partner says "YES." This means that it is either the ace, 2, 3 or 4 of diamonds.

"It's a diamond" and your partner says "YEP" which can only mean the 3.

You say, much to the amazement of all "IT'S THE 3 of DIAMONDS!"

4. A FEAT IN BALANCING

The next time you go to a party try this on the host—if he is a good natured soul—and watch the fun. Tell him that you heard that he was good at balancing things and get some girl that he is a little sweet on to ask him to balance a pan of water on a broomstick. Of course he'll say he can't but you show him how. Stand on a step ladder and hold a pan or a glass of water flat against the ceiling. Now ask your host if he can hold that pan or glass against the ceiling with a broom handle. Tell him it is quite a difficult stunt and get him anxious to show off. When he does do it and is standing on the ladder with the broom handle pressed against the bottom of the pan or glass, say to the other guests: "Fine, now let's go home. We've had a swell time thanks." and pretend to leave him there and see what happens!

In case you do not want to take a chance with a glass or a bowl full of water balanced up against the ceiling, have your friend sit at a table with his hands out on the table, palms down. Now place a glass full of water on the back of each of his hands and tell him to balance these. When you have done this it is your cue to leave him alone and see what happens.

5. NAMING THE CARDS

Here is a fine old card trick that will mystify everyone who doesn't know it. Before you can do it you must learn a very simple short poem. This is the poem:

> 8 Kings threaten to save
> 95 Queens for 1 sick knave!

Say this over and over again until you know it thoroughly. Now look at the code:

> 8, King, 3, 10 (threaten) 2, 7 (save)
> 9, 5, Queen, 4, 1, 6, Jack (knave)

This includes the thirteen cards and all you need do is arrange the pack before hand in that order, namely: 8 K 3 10 2 7 9 5 Q 4 Ace 6 J. As you do this be sure that the suits are: Spade, Heart, Diamond and Club and repeat.

Now put the pack face down on the table and say to everyone "The first card that I will turn up is the 8 of Spades." Turn it up. "The next will be the King of Hearts" Turn it up. "The next will be the 3 of Diamonds" Turn it up. "The next will be the 10 of Clubs" Turn it up. "The next will be the 2 of Spades," etc.—

You can go right through the pack this way and nobody will catch on to the trick.

6. CIGARETTE MAGIC

Select four of the most popular brands of cigarettes and a glass. Choose a confederate and both you and he learn the following code:

CAMEL........right hand over top of glass—glass upright

CHESTERFIELD........left hand over top of glass—glass upright

LUCKY STRIKE........right hand over top of glass—glass upside down

OLD GOLD........left hand over top of glass—glass upside down

When you both know this code sufficiently you are ready to do the trick. Have your partner go inside and wait. Now ask anyone in the room to light any one of the four brands of cigarettes and puff the smoke into the glass. He lights a Camel and puffs the smoke into the glass which you are holding. You immediately place your hand over the top of the glass and hand it to him to take inside to your partner. In handing him the covered glass you naturally see that he is holding it in accordance with the above code. Tell him to take it exactly the way he has it in to your partner and he will name the cigarette just by looking at the smoke. And sure enough, your partner names it!

7. A SIMPLE CARD TRICK

This trick can only be done with a pack of cards whose backs are not the same upside down as they are right side up. There are any number of packs like this—where pictures appear on the backs of the cards instead of designs. If you happen to have

[214]

a pack of this description, all you need do is arrange all the cards so that the pictures are the same way. This is done, of course, before your guests arrive, or you can do it quickly without anyone observing you, after they have arrived.

Form the pack into a fan shape and ask someone to take a card out. As soon as he has done this, even the pack up again and ask that person to look at his card and show it to everyone but not to you. Now, without anyone noticing, turn the pack of cards around in your hand so that when your friend puts the card he has chosen back into the pack it will be the only card *whose back is upside down*. When he has done this, you may shuffle the cards all you wish—it makes no difference, of course—and tell him that you will name his card.

Now, here is where the fun comes in! Holding the pack of cards in your left hand, with the backs up, and starting with the top card, go through the pack slowly, turning each card face up and noting that the picture on the back of each card is always in the same position. As soon as you come to a back which is upside down (the only back which is upside down in the whole pack), note what card it is when you turn it face up, *but say nothing about it*. Keep going for another five or six cards and then stop and say: "I will bet you five dollars the next card that I turn *over* will be your card." Of course, your friend will bet you, because he has already seen his card passed over and you have said nothing about it. Everybody else in the room will bet you too, and think that you have missed out. When you are ready, all you need do is go back among the cards which are face up, pick up his card (which you know) and turn it over. You will win the bet.

To take an example, suppose your friend takes the ten of diamonds. He puts it in the pack, and it is the only card whose back is upside down. As you go through the cards, turning each one face up, you come to the one that is upside down, and you notice when you turn it face up that it is the ten of diamonds. You say to yourself, "That is his card," but you keep on going just the same, without saying a word to anyone. After you have turned another five or six cards face up, stop and, remembering the ten of diamonds, inform everyone that the next card that you are going to turn over will be the chosen card. When everyone bets you, all you need do is go back and turn the ten of diamonds over.

8. A BAFFLING CARD TRICK

This is a baffling card trick which few people can catch on to, yet it is extremely simple.

Cut a pack of cards unequally, and remove the smaller cut. Now cut the new pile into unequal parts and give your friend the smaller part and you take the greater. Tell him to count the number of cards in his pile, and you will do the same. Count the number of cards in your hand. Now say to him, "I have as many cards as you have, and enough more to make 19 and 2 over." Now start counting cards together—each time you put down a card, he puts down a card, face down. As you have more cards than he, he will be out of cards at some point, say 14. When this point is reached, say: "I said I'd have enough more to make 19 —that means 5"—(now count 1, 2, 3, 4, 5)—then stop and show two cards left over, which is just what you said you had.

This will always mystify everyone, but it is ridiculously simple. The catch lies in the words, "enough to make." For example: Suppose you have 24 cards and he has 15. It makes no difference how many cards he has, as long as he has less than you. You count your cards and see that you have 24, which is really 20 and 4 left over, 21 and 3 left over, or any other number you choose to mention, but don't have more than 4 cards left over. Now you can see that no matter how many cards he has, you will have just what you say you have, namely 24 cards. You do not say you have 24 cards, however, you say you have enough more cards to make 21 and 3 left over, or 22 and 2 left over, etc. The amount of cards he has makes no difference, except that it confuses the issue and makes it look as though you knew how

many cards he had. If he has 15 cards, you count with him up to
15, then say: "I said I would have enough more to make 22—
that's 7" and count the 7 cards. Stop there and exhibit the two
remaining cards in your hand to prove that what you said was
true.

It is more important to get your statement accurate. Be sure
to say, "I have as many cards in my hand as you have in yours,
and enough more to make so much with so much left over."

9. CARD CODE TRICK

This is an old trick but not very well known. It is one of the
most effective that we know of. It is done with 36 cards laid out
face up in six squares of six cards each. (See diagram p. 218). Before you go out of the room, make sure that someone in the room
understands the trick so that he can signal you, in an offhand
manner. While you are out of the room, someone in the room
selects one of the 36 cards without touching it. You come back
and your confederate might say, as a passing remark to somebody in the room, "I had chicken for lunch," which immediately will tell you that the card is the ace of hearts.

Now how does this work? It is extremely simple. The 36
cards are divided into the following categories in order:

1. Man   3. Beast   5. Fowl
2. Woman   4. Fish   6. Insect

The first six (3 columns of 2 cards each) having to do with
man, the second six having to do with woman, the third six having to do with beast, the fourth six having to do with fish, the
fifth six having to do with fowl, and the last six having to do
with insects.

Each one of the six cards in each group is also divided into
these categories, which makes it extremely simple. The second
card in the first group is obviously MAN-WOMAN—so that
if your confederate is a man and he says, "I met Helen yesterday," you know it is MAN-WOMAN, the second card or the
queen of clubs.

Your friend, in this case, said, "I had chicken for lunch," which means MAN-FOWL, placing the card as number 5 in the first group. Suppose your card were the second card in the fourth group (the 9 of clubs), your confederate would then have to say something involving first a fish and then a woman.

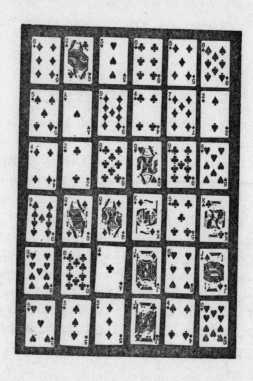

He might say "Sea bass never agrees with my wife." This immediately gives you FISH-WOMAN combination. The diagram will serve to make this clear.

Be sure that no one knows that your confederate knows anything about the trick. Make it appear as though he is merely entering into conversation with other people. The other guests will also make remarks, which you may disregard. You only pay attention to his first statement and get the combination immediately. You do not need to select the card right away. You can let other people talk before you do so, as this will add to the mystery of the trick.

10. MIND-READING

This is a mean trick—don't carry it too far. Test the various guests' psychic powers by sending several persons in turn out of the room, one at a time, while the entire group concentrates on some object to be named. As each returns to the group and tries to guess what the object is, he will naturally fail, unless telepathy is more developed than we think it is, if he succeeds right off, it is quite spooky—but he won't. Having shown up how poor the psychic qualities of these two or three guests are, you select some player who is good-natured and whom you wish to make the "goat." Make him leave the room and while he is out tell the crowd that whatever object he selects will be the one. Have everyone agree to this. When he comes back, he will name an object, and everyone will marvel at his skill, congratulate him, and tell him how wonderful he is. Send him out again and let him miss one or two times before you all congratulate him, so that he won't get wise to the trick you are playing on him. If he succeeded immediately two or three times in succession, he might get on to the trick. Never let it go more than three questions. Everyone will have a good laugh, and the person who is the "goat" will think he is marvelous until he learns the secret.

11. CARD SPELLING

Select 13 cards, from the ace to the king inclusive, from a pack, and arrange them as follows: 3, 8, 7, ace, queen, 6, 4, 2, jack, king, 10, 9, and 5. This order should be memorized carefully. When you have the cards arranged thus, all you need do is spell them out, to the astonishment of your guests.

Holding this little pack in your left hand, take the top card, and without looking at it place it on the bottom and say "O." Now take the next top card and do the same thing, only this time say "N." Do the same with the next card and say "E." Now *remove the next card,* (which will be the ace) and you have

O-N-E—1. When you put the ace on the table face up, say "one." Now continue just as you did before, spelling T-W-O—2, but when you come to the card that should be two, throw it on the table face up, just as you did the ace, and say "two." Continue to spell T-H-R-E-E, always taking the top card and putting it underneath. After you have spelled three, the next card will be the three, which you throw down on the table face up. This continues until you have nothing but the king and queen in your hand. These cards go from top to bottom alternately as you spell Q-U-E-E-N and drop the queen face up as the next card. The last card, of course, will be the king.

12. TELEPHONE CARD TRICK

After the guests are all seated take out a pack of cards, from which all aces, 5's and 9's have been removed, and shuffle it thoroughly. Now ask anyone in the room to take a card and show it to everyone in the room. As soon as he does this tell him to go to the telephone and call up a certain number which you will give him and ask for Dr. so-and-so and he will tell what card was selected. This trick actually works!

Suppose one of your guests selects the 2 of Spades. After showing this card to everyone in the room he goes inside, and, at your direction, calls Main 4725 and asks for Dr. Bates. As soon as "Dr. Bates" answers the telephone your friend says:

"Is this Dr. Bates?"
(*Voice at the other end of the phone*) "Yes."
"What card do I hold in my hand, Doctor?"
(*Voice*) "The 2 of Spades!"

Of course as many guests as care to, may witness this truly amazing telephone conversation to see that it is the real thing and no put up job.

The trick is very simple. It is merely a code that you have with one or two friends who don't happen to be at the party.

The vowels a, e, i, and o are the four suits in that order. A is Spades. E is Hearts. I is Diamonds and O is Clubs. The face value of the card is the letter number in the alphabet (without vowels) for example:

```
1 2 3 4 5 6 7 8 9 10 J Q K
* B C D * F G H * J K L M
```

The first 2 letters of the doctor's name give the clue. Dr. Bates immediately told your friend at the other end of the phone (who knows this code) two letters: B and A. Now B stands for 2 and A is the Spade suit therefore the instant he heard "Dr. Bates?" he said to himself "2 of Spades."

It is up to you to make up these names as the cards are picked. Here are a few examples:

Dr. Getton—7 of Hearts (GE)
Dr. Mole—King of Clubs (MO)
Dr. Jinks—10 of Diamonds (JI)

In case you live in a small town and there is a chance of someone in the room recognizing the phone number and yelling out "That's not a doctor's phone number—that's Harry Smith's house" all you need do is arrange with your friend beforehand to be at the corner drug store at a certain time and wait at the pay telephone booth for your call. Then it is a simple matter if you know the number of the pay telephone in that drug store. Nobody will catch on because this number will not be familiar at all!

Be sure you remove all the aces, fives and nines from the pack before you do this trick.

13. BOY, WHAT A MEMORY!

Here is a wonderful memory trick which is sure to make everyone envious until he finds out how it is done!

Copy the following numbers on a piece of paper and tell your guests that a recent memory course has enabled you to memorize

50 of 100 different 10 digit numbers. This would be a remarkable thing to do if it were legitimate so don't let anyone know how you do it and watch them gasp with admiration! Here are a few of the numbers just to get you started—you can work out the rest when you know the simple system. Work them out up to 50 when you know the system.

1. 3145943707
2. 4156178538
3. 5167303369
4. 6178538190

5. 7189763921
6. 8190998752
7. 9101123583
8. 0224606628

Let anyone name any circled number and you will give the large number opposite it. For example someone may say 27. You think awhile and then say 9325729101. Someone may say 3. You think awhile and then say 5167303369. Here is how it works:

As soon as you hear the number mentally add 12 to it and reverse the digits. Now mentally add these digits together and place the result to the right as the next digit and so on. Take 3 for example. If you add 12 you get 15 and, reversing this you get 51 which is the number you start off with. Now 5 + 1 is 6, therefore 6 is the next digit. 6 + 1 is 7 and 7 is the next digit. Now 7 + 6 is 13 so 3 is the next digit (disregard the 10). Now 3 + 7 is 10 so 0 is the next digit (disregard the 10). 3 + 0 is 3 which is the next digit, 3 + 3 is 6 which is the next digit and 6 + 3 is 9 which is the last digit!

Here is another to make sure that you have the system: Take 37:

37 + 12 is 49. Reverse this and get 94
Now start off with 94 and the next digit is 3 (9 + 4 is 13)
Now you have 943
Now 3 + 4 is 7 and the next digit is 7
Now you have 9437
Now 7 + 3 is 10 and the next digit is 0
Now you have 94370

You can see that this can go on indefinitely but you must carry it out to only 10 places—which is plenty! You don't remember the number, all you do is call off the digits one at a time.

In making up this list of 50 numbers don't have it consecutive. Have it all mixed up so that nobody will see the 31, 41, 51 etc. which is very noticeable when the numbers are in rotation.

14. A MORE DIFFICULT CARD TRICK
By Royal Heath

Slip the following four cards into your pocket unnoticed:
ACE OF SPADES
TWO OF HEARTS
FOUR OF DIAMONDS
EIGHT OF CLUBS

Be sure that they are in this order so that when you put your hand in your pocket you will know that the Ace of Spades is the first card, the Two of Hearts is the second card, etc.

Now have somebody shuffle the cards and cut the pack face down. Tell him to take a card from one of the two packs and show it to everyone and then put it back. After this has been done you take the other pack and, putting it in your pocket (carefully on top of the four cards that you already have there) ask what the card was. When you hear the card you put your hand into your pocket (where everyone saw you put the other half of the pack) and pull out a card of the same suit as the selected card. Now tell everyone that you will pull out another card or two more cards which will add up to the card selected. This you do to the astonishment of the crowd!

Here is what you do: Remembering that the combinations of 1, 2, 4 and 8 will make any number up to 13 (king) and knowing just where these cards are in your pocket as just described, all you need do is a little mental arithmetic. Suppose the card selected is the 9 of Hearts. You know right away that the second card in order in your pocket is a Heart (the Two of Hearts)

[223]

so you pull out the second card and say "That's your suit." Now all you need do is add 1 and 8 to get 9 so the next two cards that you pull out of your pocket will be the Ace of Spades and the Eight of Clubs and these will add up to 9! Do this and say "That adds up to your card."

In spite of the fact that half the shuffled pack is in your pocket and you have *called everyone's attention to this fact,* this does not interfere with the four original cards which are on the bottom, in the order named. Suppose the card chosen is the 5 of Spades. You first bring out the ace (the bottom card in your pocket) and say "That's your suit." Now go to the third card and bring out the 4 of Diamonds which, with the ace will add to 5!

Don't do this trick more than twice in one evening. Learn it and practice it before you attempt it.

15. EASY WHEN YOU KNOW HOW

Without anyone seeing you, remove the following four cards from a pack: 2, ace, 7, and 8. Put these on the top of the pack so that the 2 is the top card, the ace is the next, the seven is the next and the eight is the 4th card. You realize, of course, that you can shuffle this pack without disturbing these four top cards, provided you shuffle them in your hands instead of in two piles, as is usual.

Shuffle the cards in this manner and select someone from the crowd. Tell him to take a number between 100 and 1000. There must be no zeros in the number, no repetition of digits, and the difference between the first and the last digit must be greater than 1—172, for example, does not count because the difference between 1 and 2 is not greater than 1. This leaves a wide range of numbers to choose from.

After he has selected his number, he must reverse the first and last digit—if he took 219 he must write 912, if he took 378 he must write 873, etc., and subtract one from the other. Now he must take the lesser from the greater, and he will get a new number in three digits. Tell him now to do the same thing with this new number, only instead of subtracting, add. For example, if his new number is 479, he is to add 974. As soon as he gets his answer, tell him to multiply it by 2. Here is the way he does it:

Suppose he took 874:
He writes down 874, and under it writes 478, thus

$$
\begin{array}{r}
874 \\
478 \\
\hline
396
\end{array}
$$

He takes one from the other and gets 396
Now he reverses 396 and gets 693.
He adds 693 to 396 ....
$$
\begin{array}{r}
693 \\
\hline
1089
\end{array}
$$

He now multiplies this by 2 and gets 2178.

No matter what numbers he takes, provided they obey the rules in the second paragraph, he will always get 2178.

16. THE CLOCK TRICK

Arrange the cards in a circle exactly like a clock, placing the ace where the 1 would be, the 2 where the 2 would be, etc. and, of course, the jack and queen will take the place of 11 and 12. You now have a "clock of cards."

Tell someone to select one of those cards and, starting on lucky seven, he must count with you until you stop. You will stop at the card he chose. When he starts to count he must start with the number of the card that he selected. If he selected four, he must start with four and keep right on counting to himself up to 19.

Now look at the diagram (next page) and see how cards are laid out. Suppose your friend selects the four of spades (the suit doesn't matter) starting on card number 7 you tell him to count *to himself* as you go from card to card. Card number 7 is his 4. Now you point to card number 6 (this is his 5). Now you point to card number 5 (this is his 6) and each card you point to in succession he counts successively. If you stop him at the 19th card it will be his. Try it out and verify it.

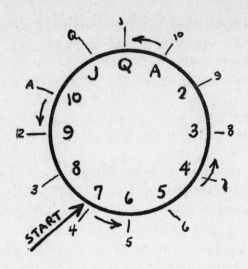

17. PSYCHIC QUESTIONS

This is a splendid trick which must not be done with less than eight people.

Have everyone in the room write a question which he wants answered. Now all papers are folded several times and dropped into a hat which you pass around.

Now seat yourself at a table at one end of the room with your guests at the other end, and, with the hat of folded papers on the table in front of you and a trash basket handy, start your psychic reading.

Now pull out one of the folded pieces of paper and, without unfolding it, hold it against your head and pretend to read the question "mentally," giving either a sensible or a foolish answer. As soon as you have done this open up the paper and read what is written on it. Now scramble the paper up and throw it in the basket and choose another paper from the hat and, without opening it go through the same performance all over again reading the question "mentally" and answering it. Continue this until nearly all of the questions have been answered, much to the astonishment of everyone.

Unless you have tried this trick you have no idea what an effect it produces. It looks exactly as though you had psychic powers and could read through the papers—but don't do the trick more than once in an evening. Here is the way it works:

Everyone has written a question and there are as many questions in the hat as there are people playing. Because there are more than eight people doing this trick the first question will go unnoticed. It is really the only fake question and you must make it up. It does not belong to anyone in the room and, since you don't call attention to it, each person will think it is the other one's question and it will go unnoticed. After you have "mentally" read and answered this fake question, open the paper and read the real question which is written on it, then scramble the paper up and throw it away. From now on it is very easy. To each paper that you pull out of the hat and hold against your forehead you apply the question which you read on the previous paper and it is impossible to tell the difference! As you finish "mentally" reading each question, answering it and asking the person who wrote it to stand up and verify it, you "check up" on your own psychic powers by opening up this question and "seeing if you were correct." Of course what you really are doing is reading the question which you must ask next but nobody realizes it.

You are always one jump behind the next paper but nobody knows it and, since you throw all these papers away there is no way of finding out. The only part of this trick to be careful about is the first question which you must make up yourself.

18. MORE THAN A COINCIDENCE

This startling trick is done with three coins: a half dollar, a quarter and a penny. It must be done by two people who know the code.

The first person (a man) leaves the room and everyone agrees on a number between 1 and 150. The man is called back and the girl (the other person who knows the trick) places the three coins on the back of a magazine for the man to look at. He looks at them and tells the number selected!

The trick is extremely simple. The magazine on which the coins are placed really represents an imaginary clock. With this in mind remember that whatever number the half dollar is on must be squared. Whatever number the quarter is on must be added to this (if heads) and subtracted (if tails). The penny is merely used to confuse the audience. It has no meaning at all.

Suppose the number selected were 86. The nearest square to 86 is 9 so the half dollar is placed where the 9 on the imaginary clock would be. Now we must add 5 to this so the quarter is placed on the 5 of the imaginary clock (heads up). The penny may be placed anywhere as it doesn't count.

Suppose 97 were chosen. 97 is really 10 squared minus 3, hence the half dollar goes on 10 and the quarter goes on 3 (tails up).

If the number chosen is a perfect square put the quarter on top of the half dollar and put both coins on the square root of the number. If it is 49 put both coins on 7, if it is 64 put both coins on 8, etc.

Suppose the number 2 is taken. 2 is really 2 squared minus 2. The half dollar goes on 2 and the quarter below it (toward the center of the clock) so that both coins are next to one another and the quarter is tails up. A better way to show this would be 3 squared minus 7. The half dollar on 3 and the quarter (tails up) on 7.

If negative numbers are chosen turn the half dollar tails up. No fractions are allowed.

19. A GOOD NUMBER TRICK

On a piece of paper write down any number between 1 and 50. Now fold the paper and give it to one of the guests in the room to hold, without looking at it. If you give it to a boy, tell him to put it in his pocket.

Now select anyone in the room and ask him to take a number

between 50 and 100, without letting you see it. When he has done this, tell him to add to the number which he has taken another number which you will give him. When he has done that tell him that he will have a number between 100 and 200 and he will agree with you. Now tell him to cross off the left hand digit, which is 1, and add it to the remaining digits—if, for example, he has 135, he is to cross off the 1, add it to the 35 and get 36. As soon as he has done that, tell him to subtract this from his original number and watch the fun when you tell the boy to whom you gave the slip of paper to open it up. The numbers will agree!

This is how it is done:

The number that you tell you friend to add is always 99 minus the number you wrote on the paper. Be sure to remember this as it is very important. If you wrote 43 on the paper, you must tell him to add 56. If you wrote 34 on the paper, you must tell him to add 65.

Here is what happens behind the scenes:

WHAT YOU DO	WHAT YOUR FRIEND DOES
1. You write down any number less than 99 (say 23) on a piece of paper; fold it, and hand it to your friend, telling him not to look at it.	He slips the paper into his pocket without looking at it.
2. Tell him to write down any number between 50 and 100 without letting you see it.	He writes 86
3. You subtract the number you wrote on the piece of paper (23) from 99 mentally, and tell your friend to add 76 to his number.	He adds: 86 76 ——— 162
4. Tell him to cross off the first number and add it to the result.	He does so: 162 1 ——— 63
5. Now tell him to subtract his result from the original number and look at the folded piece of paper you gave him.	He subtracts: 86 63 ——— 23

20. LIE DETECTOR

Try this trick on the men first, because girls are quite sensitive about their age.

This is a great way of telling whether the person is telling the truth about his or her age.

The trick is so simple that a ten year old child can do it and you can be an expert lie detector in less than five minutes. Here is what you tell your guests to do:

First, write down your present age (by the end of this year)
Second, add to this your age next year
Third, multiply by 5
Fourth, add the last digit of the year in which you were born. If you were born in 1918, add 8; if you were born in 1912 add 2, etc.
Fifth, tell me the result.

When you hear this number, take 5 from it. The result will always be a number of three digits, the first two of which tell the age.

To find out whether your friends are telling the truth or not, deduct the last digit from the last two digits of the present year (37) and consider the last digit only. If this agrees with the third digit in the number given to you, your friend is telling the truth. If it doesn't, he or she lied.

Here is exactly what happens behind the scenes:

What to Tell Your Victim to Do	The Truth SAM is 27		A Lie FLO is 29	
1. Write down your age (up to the end of this year). Don't tell it to me.	Sam writes	27	Flo writes	22
2. Add to this your age next year.	Sam adds	27 28 55	Flo adds	22 23 45
3. Multiply by 5.	Sam multiplies 5 × 55 = 275		Flo multiplies 5 × 45 = 225	

4. Now say quickly: "Of course you know the year you were born —add the last digit of this year to your result."	Sam figures he was born in 1906 so he adds 6 to 275	Flo, taken off her guard, knows she was born in 1904 but, feeling that the last digit can't give her away, adds 4 to 225
5. Ask Sam and Flo for their results.	Sam announces 281	Flo announces 229

Take Sam first: Deduct 5 from 281 = 276 and note the first 2 digits (27) which is the age Sam wrote down. Now subtract the remaining digit (6) from the last digit of this year (1933) and you have

$$1933 \\ \underline{-6} \\ 7$$

This 7 and the 7 of 27 are the same. That means Sam told the truth.

Now take Flo: Do the same with Flo. Subtract 5 from her 229 = 224. Note the first 2 digits 22 which is the age Flo gave herself. Now take the last digit (4) from the last digit of 1933 and you get

$$1933 \\ \underline{-4} \\ 9$$

This 9 represents the second digit in her true age. As this 9 and the 2 of the 22 do not agree, we know Flo lied. She said she was 22 and she is really 29. Deceptive Flo!

Now let us summarize this trick step by step.
1. Write down your present age (up to the end of this year).
2. Add to this your age next year.
3. Multiply by 5.
4. Add the last digit of the year of your birth.
5. Tell me the result.

When you hear this number deduct 5 from it. The result will always be a number of three digits, the first two of which give you the age your friend wrote down.

To find out whether or not he told the truth merely subtract the third digit from the last two digits of the present year ('33) and consider the last figure only. For example, after deducting 5 from the number Sam gave you, you have 276. You know instantly that he said he was 27 and if you deduct 6 from 33 and consider the last digit only of this answer, you'll have 7. Compare this with the last number of his age—if it corresponds your friend told the truth. In this case he did. If, in the case of Flo, the final number does not correspond to the last digit of her age, you'll know your friend did not tell the truth. You will also know how much he or she lied.

1. ROLL YOUR OWN

A five gallon jug or earthenware crock is put on the floor on its side. On one side of it on the floor put a package of cigarettes and on the other side a box of matches.

A volunteer is chosen to sit on the jug. He crosses one leg over the other with only one heel touching the floor. Now he must pick up a cigarette and put it in his mouth and then pick up the matches and light the cigarette without rolling off the jug. If you think this is easy try it!

2. HARD BOILED MILK

Boil an egg for fifteen minutes and then remove the shell. Now place the egg on the mouth of a milk bottle and bet your friends that you can make the egg go through the mouth of the bottle without breaking the egg.

It is very simple and quite spectacular. Merely set fire to a crumpled up piece of paper inside the milk bottle and just before the paper starts to burn place the egg over the mouth of the bottle as before. You will see the egg gradually go through the mouth of the bottle and drop into the bottle!

You can also soak the egg—shell and all—in vinegar and let it stand overnight. Then the whole egg will go through, shell and all. This stunt can also be done with a banana partly peeled. The banana will peel itself.

3. THE FOUR WRONG QUESTIONS

Bet anyone that he can't answer four questions, which you will ask him, incorrectly. When he takes your bet try the following:

    1. When did Columbus discover America?
           He may say 1937 and score 1 wrong.
    2. How many States are there in the Union?
           He may say 109 and score 2 wrong.

Now hesitate before you ask the next question:

3. How much is 18 and 6?
   He may say 47 and score 3 wrong.

Now hesitate some more, then very nonchalantly and rather suddenly say:
"Let's see—how many questions is that so far?"
   He, taken off his guard, will say 3, which will be the correct answer!

4. WRONG AGAIN!

Here's another one somewhat like the previous one.

Bet anyone that he can't name the next highest number to some numbers which you will give him and have every one correct. When he takes you up, name a lot of numbers, starting with two digits and gradually going up to three digits and finally four digits. For example:

    51. He will say 52
    94. He will say 95
   106. He will say 107
   328. He will say 329
   763. He will say 764
   1397. He will say 1398
   2554. He will say 2555
   3762. He will say 3763
   4099. If he is like everyone else he'll say 5000!

Be sure to say these numbers correctly. If your number is 2374, say: "Two thousand three hundred and seventy-four" instead of two-three-seven-four. When you come to the catch number, 4099, say "Four thousand and ninety-nine" and not "Four-O-nine-nine."

Of course it makes no difference what numbers you take as long as you lead your friend GRADUALLY to the catch number, 4099. Always start low and work up gradually, pausing in between numbers to imply that you are thinking hard and demanding a very quick response from your friend in each case.

[233]

5. IT'S ALWAYS 30!

Tell your friend to write down any digit from 1 to 6 inclusive and you will do the same and always make the total add up to 30! He can go first or you can go first—it makes no difference. Try it any number of times and watch your friend's amazement —but don't tell him how it is done. Here is the secret:

If HE goes first you will have 8 numbers and you must see that the first pair add up to 9 and the other pairs add up to 7 each. Obviously 9 plus 7 plus 7 plus 7 equals 30.

If YOU go first be sure to write either 1 or 2. No matter what number he adds you can always make 9 from it—and then go on from there. Here are a few examples: The regular type is you, the italics your friend:

He goes first:

$$6 + 3 + 2 + 5 + 4 + 3 + 3 + 4 = 30$$
$$1 + 2 + 4 + 2 + 5 + 2 + 6 + 1 + 1 + 6 = 30$$

(Note that in this case it took four digits to make the first 9. When your friend said 1 you had to add a number less than 3 since 1 plus 3 or more would be greater than 9 if your friend should add 6 as his next number)

You go first:

$$2 + 3 + 4 + 6 + 1 + 5 + 2 + 4 + 3 = 30$$
$$1 + 6 + 2 + 3 + 4 + 6 + 1 + 2 + 5 = 30$$

6. EGG SPINNING

Boil two eggs for about fifteen minutes before the guests arrive. Mark one of these eggs with a tiny pencil mark so that you know it's *your* egg. After the guests come show them all how easy it is to spin an egg on its bottom by doing it with your egg. Now give anyone who wants to try it the other egg and defy him to do it. He won't be able to no matter how hard he tries—nor will anyone else!

The secret is in the boiling. The egg which you marked as yours should be held upright in the water while boiling. This can be done with the aid of two teaspoons. Be sure to keep it in a vertical position while it is being boiled because this causes the air in the egg to ascend to the top, making the bottom heavier than the top and enabling you to spin it on its bottom as shown. The other egg, of course, is just boiled in the ordinary way.

7. EATING A CANDLE

Have a short candle burning in a candlestick at one end of the room. Don't let anyone too near to it. While everyone is engaged in conversation, say loudly: "I'm awfully hungry—hungry enough to eat a candle, wick and all!" Now go over to the candle, blow it out and eat it up to the complete amazement of everyone!

The secret is that the candle is not a real candle. It is a piece of banana with a thinly sliced piece of beechnut or butternut for a wick. This may be lit, for a beechnut or a butternut will burn nicely for two or three minutes. The whole thing will look just like a burning candle if you don't get too close to it and when you pick it up and eat it whole, chewing and swallowing it, the illusion is excellent. Try it!

8. CUTTING A PEAR WITHOUT TOUCHING IT!

It's quite a stunt to cut a pear in half without touching it with your hand or with a knife, but you can do it. After everyone is sure that you can't possibly do this thing, tie a string to the stem and hang it up as high as you can. You can thumb tack the string to the ceiling and allow the pear to hang, like a pendulum, for not more than a foot. Now let someone hold a sharp carving knife on the floor, knife edge up, directly under the pear. All you need do now is to light a match and apply it to the string or, if you want to be less dramatic, cut the string with a scissors. The pear will fall with quite a little force and the knife will cut it in half.

[235]

9. MAKING PAPER STAND WITHOUT TOUCHING IT!

Here is a real stunt which nobody will believe is possible. How can anyone stand a flat piece of thin paper on its edge for a minute or two without touching or creasing the paper? It sounds ridiculous doesn't it? But here is how it is done:

Take a piece of thin paper about 3" wide by 5" high and lay it flat on a table. Now take out your pocket comb and rub it vehemently on your coat or run it violently through your hair. After you have done this for about 10 seconds, bring the comb near one edge of the paper. The paper will immediately rise and you will be able to control it with the comb, making it stand on edge! This trick is good only in winter. The colder the day, the better it will work.

10. THE NICKEL AND THE QUARTER

Place three coins on a table—a nickel, a penny and a quarter. The penny is to be in between the nickel and the quarter. All three coins must touch one another. You can move the nickel but you mustn't touch it; you can touch the penny but you mustn't move it. The problem is to put the quarter between the nickel and the penny.

The solution is very simple. All you need do is press heavily with one finger upon the penny and, with a finger of the other hand, knock the quarter up against the penny, thus knocking the nickel out of place. If you do this hard enough, there will be a big enough space between the nickel and the penny for the quarter to go. If you examine this, you will find that you have touched the penny but not moved it, have moved the nickel but not touched it, and have placed the quarter between the penny and the nickel.

11. THE DIME UNDER THE QUARTER

Place a quarter and a dime on a bridge table. The problem is to put the dime under the quarter without touching the quarter.

This seems impossible until you take the dime and hold it directly under the spot on the table where the quarter lies. (Hold the dime under the table.)

12. BLINDFOLD TEST FOR CIGARETTES

This is a stunt which is sure to keep people guessing. Before the guests arrive take a package of Lucky Strikes or Old Golds or Camels (it makes no difference which you select) and dip both ends of each cigarette in a pasty concoction of moistened flour and salt. Be sure to get very little on each cigarette or else you will give the secret away, but the object is to have both ends of the cigarette a little salty without anyone noticing that anything is wrong.

Now mix all these cigarettes up together—Camels, Luckies, Old Golds and any other brand, and when the guests arrive blindfold yourself, tell them you will take a cigarette test. You will tell whether the cigarette you are smoking is or is not an Old Gold (or whatever brand you select). Now select a cigarette and start to smoke it. Feel around with your tongue and if it tastes the least bit salty you will know it is an Old Gold (or whatever brand you were going to name.) If it does not, all you need to say is, "This is not an Old Gold."

This is a very simple stunt and nobody will catch on to it.

13. HERE'S HOW!

This is by no means a new stunt but it is one of the most popular. It is otherwise known as Colonel Puff.

It is up to you as the host or hostess, to learn it thoroughly—practice it at your leisure until you know it very well from memory, then you will be ready to have a great deal of fun with your guests.

All you need for the Here's How Stunt, is a bridge table, a chair, a large serving tray, a small pitcher and a small glass. If your principles are such that you will not touch alcohol or intoxicating drinks, then it is a simple matter to fill the pitcher with grape juice or lemonade—otherwise use beer or a scotch or rye highball. Now sit down to the table and tell everyone that you are going to teach them a toast to the HERE'S HOW CLUB. Tell them to watch carefully everything you do, because they are going to do it after you. If they make any mistake they will have to fill the glass all over again—and the more mistakes they make the more they will have to fill the glass (and if the glass contains something more than grape juice, the chances are that the more mistakes they make the more they will keep on making them).

Now go through your demonstration just exactly as it is given below (which you have learned from memory) and when you are through, rise and say aloud to the one particular person you select, "That's how; now *you* do it."

THE TOAST OF THE "HERE'S HOW" CLUB

(Say aloud): "HERE'S HOW!" (*Before* touching glass.)

1. Pick up glass between first finger and thumb, right hand.
2. Drink once from the glass.
3. Tap glass once on tray as you lay it down.
4. Tap on table once with 1st finger of right hand.
5. Tap on table once with 1st finger of left hand.
6. Tap right knee once with 1st finger of right hand.
7. Tap left knee once with 1st finger of left hand.
8. Tap floor once with right foot.
9. Tap floor once with left foot.
10. Rise from chair once and sit down again.

(Say aloud): "HERE'S HOW! HERE'S HOW!" (*Before* touching glass.)

1. Pick up glass with first *two* fingers and thumb, right hand.
2. Drink twice from the glass.
3. Tap glass twice on tray as you lay it down.
4. Tap on table twice with first two fingers of right hand.
5. Tap on table twice with first two fingers of left hand.

6. Tap right knee twice with first two fingers of right hand.
7. Tap left knee twice with first two fingers of left hand.
8. Tap floor twice with right foot.
9. Tap floor twice with left foot.
10. Rise from chair twice and sit down twice.

(Say aloud): "HERE'S HOW! HERE'S HOW! HERE'S HOW!" (*Before* touching glass.)

1. Pick up glass with first three fingers and thumb, *left* hand.
2. Drink three times from the glass *emptying it.*
3. Tap glass three times on tray as you lay it down.
4. Tap on table 3 times with first 3 fingers of *left* hand.
5. Tap on table 3 times with first 3 fingers of *right* hand.
6. Tap left knee 3 times with first 3 fingers of *left* hand.
7. Tap right knee 3 times with first 3 fingers of *right* hand.
8. Tap floor three times with *left* foot.
9. Tap floor three times with *right* foot.
10. Rise from chair 3 times and sit down 3 times.

(Rise and say aloud): "THAT'S HOW! NOW YOU DO IT!" (*This counts also!*)

TO THE MAN:

There's your toast! Now study until you're perfect. Then, after you've shown it and the others begin trying, you must supervise their efforts and be ready each time they make a mistake to stop them and refill the glass for another try!

CRAZY BETS

This is a "catch game" for adult evening parties. It must be played for small stakes, which are actually paid by the loser to the winner. Any player may at any time during the game, propose a FAKE BET. All the rest of the players except three who act as Judges, are obliged to bet with him. The stakes for all bets in the game are always the same amount. The player proposing the FAKE BET names one judge; the first person to take up his bet names a second judge; and these two judges name the third judge. The verdict of two out of three judges is final, as to the winner of the bet.

EXAMPLE. Kate says "I have a FAKE BET! I choose Fred as my judge and I want to bet first with Eddie."

Eddie says: "I'll bet, and I choose Vera as judge." (Fred and Vera now choose the 3rd judge, whom we will call Bob.) "Now then, Kate, what's your bet?"

Kate says: "I bet I can write a longer English word than you."

Fred tries, writing "Antidisestablishmentarianism."

Kate says: "I can write a longer English word than that; and I want to bet next with Henry." Henry is obliged to bet, under the rules. The judges remain the same as before.

Kate may thus challenge each player, and all are bound to bet the fixed stakes, unless one can win by seeing through her Fake Bet. If there is any argument, the majority opinion of the judges is final. If no one challenges successfully, Kate collects from all players, provided her own bet is acceptable to the judges. In the example just given, Kate wins by writing on a piece of paper:

"A longer English word than you" . . . or *"A longer English word than that."*

If however, someone else thought of this catch, and wrote the first phrase, Kate might still have won, if she said, "No, I mean to write a single word. I can write a longer single word than you."

Unless the challenging player catches her in this, she still may win by writing on the paper:

"A longer single word than you." (Provided the judges concur in this subterfuge being worthy of winning the bet.)

The game continues as before, after Kate has collected her winnings, or until one of the bettors puts Kate out by winning from her on a decision. Anyone may now propose another FAKE BET, and choose his judge. All players MUST bet, the stakes being always the same. Everyone has an equal chance of winning, but of course the cleverest and most deceptive

FAKE BETS are the most liable to remain unchallenged. On the other hand, players who can guess ways of out-witting the proponents of the bets may themselves win, if they get a favorable decision from the judges.

A variety of FAKE BETS is included herewith, together with the "catch" for each. (Catches are on Page 288). Think up others yourself, as you go along; but be careful to choose bets that others won't catch you at, in case you are challenged!

1. I bet I can drink the contents of this glass while the glass is under this hat, without touching the hat.
2. I bet I can hold something in my hand for three minutes that you can't hold in your hand for thirty seconds.
3. I bet I can drop a lump of sugar into a cup of coffee without wetting the sugar.
4. I bet I can turn an egg completely around in an egg-cup without touching the egg.
5. I bet I can hand you any card which you continually think of out of your own pack of cards. You may shuffle the cards as much as you wish.
6. I bet I can draw a circle of not more than 3' in diameter around you where you are now standing and you won't dare to get out of it!
7. I bet I can place two people so close together that they will be less than an inch apart yet they won't be able to touch one another.
8. I bet I can show you all something which you have never seen before and will never see again.
9. I bet I can put two different objects under two different hats, eat both objects and place them under the hats again.
10. I bet I can name a large animal that you all know that has four legs and flies.

Part IX

ANSWERS

PART I—WORD PUZZLES

BOXWORD PUZZLES

1. A 90 score:	2. A 95 score:	3. An 85 score:
S C A R E	C A P E R	A F T E R
O A S I S	A L I V E	P I A N O
I M I D E	S T A I D	R E S T A
L E D G E	H E N C E	I N T E R
S L E E T	T R O T S	L D Y R S

CONNECTOGRAMS

1. Diagram A

		GRAND	OPERA	GUIDE		
GOOSE	STEP	MOTHER		BOOK	PLATE	GLASS
		LOVE		MARK		
	SEA	SICK	BED	TIME	CLOCK	
	HORSE		CHAMBER		WORK	
	POWER	HOUSE	MAID	SERVICE	SHOP	
		HOLD		ENTRANCE		
	STOP	UP	TOWN	HALL	WAY	
	OVER	TURN		MARK	DOWN	

2. Diagram B

OPEN	SHOP	WORN	OUT	CAST
	WORK		SIDE	
GAS	BAG		SHOW	GIRL
STOVE	PIPE	DREAM	GIRL	SCOUT
GRATE		LAND		MASTER
FIRE	WATER	MARK	TIME	CLOCK
FLY	WHEEL		PIECE	WORK
	LOCK		MEAL	
STEP	IN	HOCK	TICKET	AGENT

3. Diagram C

ANTI	SOCIAL	CLUB	FOOT	LOOSE
	HALL		BRIDGE	
TRADE	MARK	TIME	TABLE	CLOTH
	UP		LAMP	
KNEE	HIGH	PITCH	BLACK	HAND
DEEP		DARK		WRITING
BLUE	SEA	HORSE	FLY	PAPER
	SIDE	CAR	WHEEL	
BOARD	WALK		LOCK	STEP

DOUBLE CROSSWORDS

Eminent Statesmen:

R	CORPSE	SCOPE	POSE	C
O	IMPLORE	RIMPLE	PRIME	L
O	ROASTED	TRADES	DARTS	E
S	SLAVE	VEAL	ALE	V
E	CREASE	ACRES	SCAR	E
V	REVEALS	SEALER	ERASE	L
E	READING	DARING	GRIND	A
L	LEARNS	SANER	EARS	N
T	DESERT	REEDS	SEER	D

Come into Court:

D	DESPAIR	ASPIRE	RAISE	P
E	FILTERED	TRIFLED	RIFTED	L
F	INFLATES	SALIENT	SILENT	A
E	EPISODE	POISED	DOPES	I
N	TENDON	TONED	DOTE	N
D	PRETEND	REPENT	PREEN	T
A	MIRAGE	GRIME	GERM	I
N	FENDER	FREED	DEER	F
T	FILAMENT	INFLAME	MENIAL	F

ANAGRAMS WITHOUT THE USE OF NEW LETTERS

PRIEST   STRIPE   SPRITE   RIPEST   ESPRIT
MATE   TEAM   TAME   MEAT
BARED   BEARD   BREAD   DEBAR
ACRES   RACES   CARES   SCARE   SACRE
MITE   EMIT   ITEM   TIME

UNTRANSPOSED ANAGRAMS

2. INTUITION—TUITION IN
3. WATCHMAN—MAN, WATCH
4. KIND MAN—MANKIND
5. CARE LESS—CARELESS
6. OF TEN—OFTEN
7. MANSLAUGHTER—MAN'S LAUGHTER
8. READ JUST—READJUST
9. SEASON—SEAS ON
10. ORATORY—OR A TORY

SAME WORD—DIFFERENT MEANINGS

2. address
3. abstract
4. invalid
5. justice—just ice
6. contract
7. wind lass—windlass
8. deserts

PROGRESSIVE ANAGRAM VERSES

AN   PAN   SNAP   PAINS   PIANOS   PASSION

TRANSPOSITIONS

1. CHRISTIANITY
2. OLD ENGLAND
3. PRESBYTERIAN
4. ASTRONOMERS
5. PENITENTIARY
6. STEP ON GAS
7. TELEGRAPH
8. DEBUTANTES
9. O DIG FLEAS
10. REMORSEFUL
11. EVERY CENT PAID ME

NONSENSE ANAGRAM VERSE

Beside the streamlet's shining band,
The fisherman sat all day.
Anon he raised a lazy hand
To drive a gnat away.
Yet, though he saw me standing by
He gave no outward sign,
But kept his keen and watchful eye
Upon his slender line.

ADDITION ANAGRAMS

1. Log-book
2. Looking-glass
3. Massacre
4. Pocket-book
5. Block-head
6. XL
7. Cross-word
8. Sensible
9. Hollywood
10. Melancholy

HIDDEN GEOGRAPHY

1.	Nile	11.	Asia
2.	Thames	12.	Delaware
3.	Ganges	13.	Chile
4.	Canada	14.	Colorado
5.	Annapolis	15.	India
6.	Armenia	16.	Maine
7.	Salem	17.	China
8.	Hartford	18.	Europe
9.	Macon	19.	Greece
10.	Seine	20.	Missouri

STRAIGHTEN THEM OUT

1. The temperature of the body is 98.6 degrees.
2. New York is the largest city in America.
3. Puppies grow into dogs and kittens into cats.
4. Mt. Everest is the highest mountain peak in the world.
5. Of all the composers Beethoven was the greatest.
6. The sum of 6 threes plus the sum of 3 sixes is the product of 6 and 6.
7. A man may be older than his uncle but can never be older than his father.
8. Albert Einstein, the most brilliant intellect in the world to-day, is a professor in Princeton.
9. Every public spirited citizen will do his duty by serving on a jury.
10. Cincinnati is not the capital of Ohio but Indianapolis is the capital of Indiana.

SAME IS DIFFERENT:

BEAMS DAMES GAMES LAMES MALES MEANS
MARES REAMS SMEAR SEAMS TAMES AMUSE

HOW ABOUT SABRE?

BRACES BEARDS BREADS BRAISE RABIES BREAKS
BAKERS BLARES BREAST BRAVES ZEBRAS

EAT YOUR WORDS

BEAT BATE BETA DATE FEAT FATE GATE
HEAT HATE LATE TALE MEAT MATE TEAM
TAME NEAT NATE ANTE ETNA PEAT PATE
TAPE RATE TEAR TARE SEAT EAST EATS
TEAS SETA

PART II—BRAIN TWISTERS

1. A COCK-EYED STORY

The expressions as they should appear in the story are:

Confirmed bachelor
Blushing bride
Proud father
Newborn baby
Blessed event
Blithering idiot
General nuisance
Traveling salesman
Tired business man
Flat tire
Absent minded Professor
Public spirited citizen
Crooked politicians

[250]

2. THE KNAUGHUPELLAR

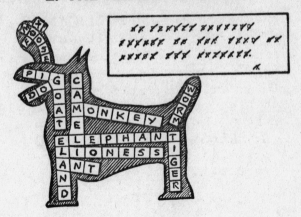

3. DESERVED

The check was for $123. 1 x 2 x 3 equals 1 + 2 + 3 and their difference is zero—which is NOT a small number.

4. MR. AND MRS. G. WATT SUCKERS

The cards, as laid out, form a code message:

1 2 3 4 5 6 7 8 9 10 J Q K
b c d f g h j k l m n p q
r s t u v w x y z
Spades—A
Hearts—E
Diamonds—I
Clubs—O

The message is: HAVE NINE HEARTS LEAD DIAMONDS

5. THE JORDAN ROBBERY

Jordan robbed himself to get the insurance. An examination of the thief's footprints shows that he could not possibly have robbed the safe. The thief entered and approached the safe but when he got there he heard the dog who came from the bedroom. He turned on his left toe and ran out the door through which he entered. The dog ran after him while Jordan entered, went over to the safe and opened it.

6. HALT AND GIVE THE COUNTERSIGN

The Key word is REPUBLICAN

1 2 3 4 5 6 7 8 9 0

If you have never *been up in an airplane,* you have a *real* thrill in store for you. The other day I went from *Pierre* to *Erie in nine* hours on a *public air line.* It was one of the biggest thrills I ever had.

7. PLEASE HELP LITTLE OTTO

$$
\begin{array}{r}
1\,1\,7 \\
3\,1\,9 \\
\hline
1\,0\,5\,3 \\
1\,1\,7 \\
3\,5\,1 \\
\hline
3\,7\,3\,2\,3
\end{array}
$$

8. EDNA'S DILEMMA

Edna remains an old maid.

9. THE HAPPY FAMILY

Four daughters and three sons.

10. THE LOGARITHMIC SPY

If you compare this with a real table of logs you will see that it is false. Since there are only 26 letters in the alphabet, any number greater than 26 is represented by its last digit, otherwise it is the last TWO digits. Now examine these numbers and you will see the clue. The last two digits of the first log are 96 which is greater than 26, hence you take only the 6. The next log has 18 for its last two digits, the next log has 65 (take only the 5). The numbers come out as follows:

6 18 5 14 3 8 4 18 9 22 5 15 14 13 5 20 etc.

This in terms of the numbered letters of the alphabet (a is 1, b is 2, etc.) gives: FRENCH DRIVE ON METZ STARTS AT TEN.

11. SALLY'S MOTHER

Sally's mother is 25; Sally is 4 years and 2 months.

12. ARE YOU SUSCEPTIBLE TO CODES?

Each digit in the numbers refers to that numbered letter in the name, thus 457682 means the 4th letter, the 5th letter, the 7th letter, the 6th letter, the 8th letter and the 2nd letter in Menstirk. This turns out to be STRIKE and the whole message is:

STRIKE VERDUN MONDAY 10 P.M.

13. SOME GANG

The party consists of two little boys and two little girls, their mother and father and both their mother's and father's parents (Their two grandfathers and two grandmothers.)

14. WHO SAID SO?

1. Keats
2. Shakespeare
3. Patrick Henry
4. Coleridge
5. Johnson
6. Bacon
7. Shakespeare
8. Emerson
9. Carroll
10. Longfellow

15. ALONE IN A CROWD

Julian married the mother of his father's second wife and had a son. His stepmother also had a son. Julian is, therefore, the father of his stepbrother's nephew, the husband of his father's mother-in-law and the father-in-law of his stepmother. He is also his own grandfather.

16. KST

The work is INKSTAND. KST is in the middle. IN is at the beginning (IN the beginning) and AND is at the end (AND at the end).

17. THE PLOT THICKENS

The Plot Thickens

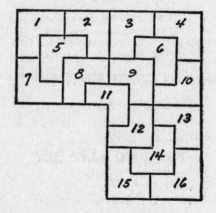

18. CAPITAL STUFF

Dick has $5005.
Both Smith and Franklin have $3755.
Dobbs has $2505.
Brewster has $1255.
Hill has $5.

19. TROUBLE IN THE BATH ROOM

5 minutes

20. THE TEA PARTY

Mrs. Mendes—the deaf woman.
Mrs. Siegel—the hostess.
Mrs. Moore—the bromidic soul.
Mrs. Newman—the woman who hates Mrs. Dix.
Mrs. Jacobs—the talkative woman.
Mrs. Dix—the fat woman.

21. THE SHOPPERS

Mrs. Adams bought the book; Mrs. Baker, the dress; Mrs. Catt, the handbag; Mrs. Dodge, the necktie; Mrs. Ennis, the lamp; Mrs. Fisk, the hat.

22. PUT THESE COLLEGE MEN IN THEIR PLACES

Johnson— Dartmouth
Barry— Yale
Brewster—Harvard
Edwards—Columbia
Adams— Princeton
Hunter— Cornell

Here is the reasoning:

Brewster is not from Cornell. Hunter is not from Columbia. Edwards is not from Harvard. Adams, the only man not discussed, must go to Princeton since Miss Kent, the only girl who hasn't a boy friend, roots for Princeton. Barry must be from Yale and Johnson must be from Dartmouth. Miss West hates Harvard men, knows Brewster and won't have anything to do with him. Brewster must be from Harvard. This leaves Hunter and Edwards for Cornell and Columbia, and since Miss Klag, who is Hunter's girl has never met any Columbia men it follows that Hunter must be from Cornell.

23. DRAMATIS PERSONNAE

Ben Gunn—Treasure Island
Uriah Heep—David Copperfield
Lucy Manette—A Tale of Two Cities
Carol Kennicott—Main Street
Catherine Barklay—A Farewell to Arms
Roxanne—Cyrano de Bergerac
Joe Harper—Tom Sawyer
Dunstan Cass—Silas Marner
Philip Bosinney—The Forsythe Saga
Edmund Dantes—The Count of Monte Cristo
John Ridd—Lorna Doone
Old Marley—Christmas Carol
Charles Strickland—The Moon and Sixpence
Sam Williams—Penrod
Amelia Sedley—Vanity Fair

24. CRYPTOGRAM

I remember, I remember
The house where I was born,
The little window where the sun
Came peeping in at morn;
He never came a wink too soon,
Nor brought too long a day,
But now, I often wish the night
Had borne my breath away!

25. WHOZOO?

Coué—father of auto-suggestion.
Thurston—magician. D
Ponzi—financier and swindler.
Amundsen—explorer. D
Sumner—book censor.
Scott—founder of "technocracy."
Sunday—evangelist. D

Lardner—novelist and short story writer. D
Kipling—famous writer and poet. D
Browning—real estate man and adopter of wives. D
Gatti-Casazza—musician.
Joyce—writer.

26. THINK COW IT IS DONE

144 cows including the neighbor's 2.

John got	48
Tom got	36
Henry got	24
Bill got	18
George got	16
	142

The sum of all the fractions does not make unity.

27. EASY AS ROLLING OFF A LOG

The total distance that Roland walked on each log is the hypotenuse of a right triangle with the length of the log as one arm and the distance that the log rolled as the other arm. The 10 foot log rolled 60 feet. The distance Roland walked on the 10 foot log is therefore the square root of $10^2 + 60^2$ which is 60.8 feet. There are 10 logs so he walked 608 feet on these logs. By similar reasoning he walked 1398 feet on the 12 foot logs, there being 30 of them. Roland therefore walked 2006 feet on all the logs and another 650 yards (1950 feet) from the bottom of the incline to the top. He therefore walked a total distance of 3956 feet.

28. THE LITERARY GANGSTER

The quotation is from Macbeth and gives the clue. Just go round and round and mark off every 31st letter paying no attention to the inside letters. Starting with G and going around to the right (clockwise) the 31st letter is M. Now start again on the next letter, I, and count off 31 letters and you will land on E. The message is:

MEET THE GANG IN NEW YORK

29. THESE STATES WANT TO BE NAMED

1. Idaho
2. Illinois
3. Maine
4. Louisiana
5. Michigan
6. Utah
7. West Virginia
8. South Carolina
9. Florida
10. Missouri
11. Mississippi
12. Tennessee
13. New York
14. New Hampshire
15. Wisconsin
16. Montana
17. Indiana
18. Kentucky
19. North Carolina
20. Ohio

30. AN H OF A PROBLEM

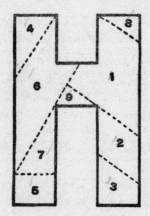

31. THE ROYAL TRIANGLE

a. From "a" we know that Card No. 3 cannot be a King.
b. From "b" we know that Card No. 2 cannot be a King.
   Therefore Card No. 1 must be a King.
c. From "c" we know that Cards Nos. 1 and 2 cannot both be Hearts.
d. From "d" we know that two Spades must come together.

Therefore Cards Nos. 1 and 2 must be Spades.

Hence the only possible answer is:
Card No. 1 ....King of Spades.
Card No. 2 ....Queen of Spades.
Card No. 3 ....Queen of Hearts.

32. UPSIDE TURVY POKER

The hand held by No. 3 is a flush, all spades, which beats the four other hands exposed in the picture. The cards are; 4, 6, 10, Queen and King of Spades.

The hand cannot be:
a. A Straight, because it wouldn't beat Hand No. 5.
b. A straight flush, because this would have to be of Spades, and several of the required cards are already exposed.
c. Four-of-a-kind, because the exposed hands contain at least one of every card-value from Ace to King inclusive.
d. (It *is* a flush).
e. A Royal Flush, because a Royal Flush can't have a Four.
f. A Full House, because this would require at least one additional Four; and all three of the remaining Fours are shown in the other hands.

33. LOONY HEADLINES

Here are the correct sentences as rewritten:
1. French navy will equal Japan's.
2. Count's horse wins Derby twice.
3. Three convicts get nine years.

34. PROBLEM IN JABBERWOCKY

THE TOLQUAT HOLDS 4 TIMES AS MUCH WATER AS THE QUATTOL.

Here is the reasoning:

If a QUATTOL is 1 DAKE in depth and a DAKE is 4 SMAGS long, then a QUATTOL is 4 SMAGS deep.

The top of a QUATTOL measures 1 SQUARE SMAG (see "c"); therefore, being 4 SMAGS deep, it holds 4 CUBIC SMAGS of water.

Now consider the TOLQUAT. Its top measures 1 DAKE by 1 DAKE; that is, 4 SMAGS by 4 SMAGS, or 16 SQUARE SMAGS. It is just 1 SMAG in depth (see "f"). Therefore it holds 16 CUBIC SMAGS of water.

Thus the TOLQUAT holds 4 times as much water as the QUATTOL.

35. I WOULDN'T TRUST HER WITH MY MONEY!

Mrs. Sucker had $45 to start with. She spent $22 for the saw, $10 for the parrot, $4 for the hair oil and $1 on buttermilk.

36. THE ETERNAL WRECTANGLE

Mr. Lamson's 3rd wife was the present Mrs. Prince, Mr. Colt's second wife was the present Mrs. Lamson. If you make a diagram as shown below letting P stand for Prince, L for Lamson etc., and the numbers 1, 2, 3 and 4 represent the order of marriage, you will come out all right. Let small letters represent the wives. The entire 4th row can be immediately filled in.

Now we know that Mrs. Lamson was Daniel's first wife so put small L under column D row 1. Mrs. Prince married Daniels a week after he divorced Mrs. Lamson, therefore put p in column D, row 2. Continue this reasoning until the remaining 12 squares are filled and you have:

	C	D	L	P
1	p	l	d	c
2	l	p	c	d
3	d	c	p	l
4	c	d	l	p

37. PERSONAL PROPERTY

Sap divided each side of the triangle into thirds and folded the middle third away from the center to form a new triangle as shown in figure 1. The second month Sap did the same thing as shown in figure 2, always adding to the perimeter an amount equal to at least 300 feet, yet the figure becomes only slightly larger.

Fig. 1.   Fig. 2.

38. FAMILY SKELETON

Number 9 vertical gives the clue. The number MUST be 43—it can't be anything else since 42 would mean that grandpa was born in 1764 and 44 would have him born in 1936. Both of these are out of the question, so the number must be 43. With this information the rest is easy:

$$
\begin{array}{c}
1\,8\,4\,9 \\
3\,7\,2\,9 \\
3\,6\,4\,4 \\
1\,3\,6\,3
\end{array}
$$

39. THE TRESTLE WALKERS

C's steps are shown as covering 7 ties, B's steps cover 5 ties and A's steps cover 6 ties. Since they all start from the same point, B and C will end up on the last tie and A will end on the next to last tie as you can easily see. The problem then is to find a number which is divisible by 7 and 5 evenly and has a remainder of 1 when divided by 6. This number is obviously 175. There are 175 ties in the trestle. The drawing shows 17½ ties to 20 feet therefore the trestle must be 200 feet long and the ties must be 1.14 + feet apart. From this information and a study of the picture you will see that A has walked 185.2 feet (13 ties less than 200 feet), B has walked 188.6 feet (10 ties less than 200 feet) and C has walked 200 feet.

40. IT'S FUN TO BE FOLD

The fold is 11.57 inches in length.

41. HIGH FINANCE

Ike had $50. Mike had $30.

42. FULL NAME PLEASE

1. Herbert George Wells
2. Gladys Bromwyn Stern
3. Gilbert Keith Chesterton
4. Henry Louis Mencken
5. Pelham Grenville Wodehouse
6. Phineas Taylor Barnum
7. Alfred Edward Housman
8. Oscar Odd McIntyre
9. Thomas Stearns Eliot
10. John Pierpont Morgan

43. COLLEGE MEN'S GOLDEN RULE

To be continually over "confident" in the midst of EXAMS dim-in-"ISHES" (diminishes) one's chances 4 6 S (for success) in "them."

44. A WEIGHTY PROBLEM

1, 3, 9, and 27 pound weights

45. QUINTUPLETS ON THE SQUARE

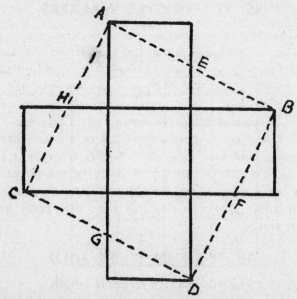

Bisect the sides of the square in E, F, G and H and draw lines as shown in the diagram. The square ABCD will then be transformed into 5 equal squares.

46. NOT SO EASY

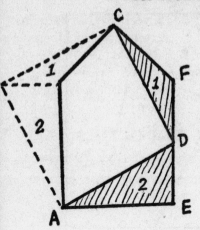

Bisect E-F in D and draw C-D and D-A. These two triangles when transposed to their new positions will transform the pentagon into a square whose sides are 6.32".

47. ON THE SQUARE

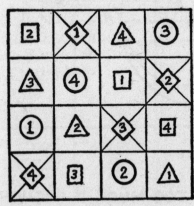

48. BETWEEN THE LINES

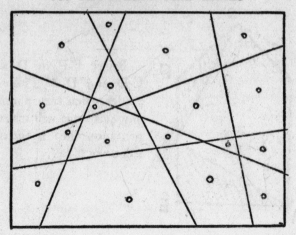

49. IT'S EASY WHEN YOU KNOW HOW

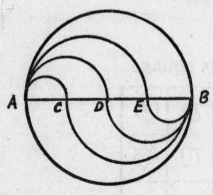

Divide diameter A B into four parts as shown and draw semicircles on A-C, A-D A-E, B-E, B-D and B-C. You have now drawn 3 lines of equal length and divided the circle into four equal parts.

50. TOO MUCH IS ENOUGH!

The word "among" applies to "more than two." Hence:

$$a + b + c \dots \dots \dots \dots = 16$$
$$a \times b \times c \dots \dots \dots \dots = 144 n \text{ (multiples of 144)}$$

One child received as much as another.

Uncle Jack must have only three children because it is impossible to have more than three numbers, the lowest of which is 4, whose sum is 16, whose product is a multiple of 144 and two of which are the same.

The only solution is, therefore, 4, 6 and 6.

Uncle Jack, therefore, gave one child $4.00 and the other two children, each $6.00

Check: $4 + 6 + 6 = 16$

$4 \times 6 \times 6 = 144$

Note, also, that 288, or any other multiple of 144, is too large for three factors to add to 16.

PART III—TEST YOURSELF

Check observation and memory games by referring to the pictures themselves.

THE SAYVILLE MURDER

1. Yes. The mail shows that it is his house and he is living there with his wife. (insert A)
2. Yes. The letter addressed to *Mrs.* Charles Leroy shows this (insert A)
3. Yes. The initials on one are his and the other is apparently a sample case showing that he was a travelling salesman.
4. Travelling Salesman. Same reason.
5. Doctor. The stethoscope shows he was a doctor and the red cross on the radiator of his car bears it out.
6. Murdered man. Same reason.
7. No. Charles Leroy lives there.
8. Probably all night. The shadow lengths show early morning and the radiator drip indicates that the car has been standing a long time.
9. No. He was just about to enter calmly when he dropped his bags and coat and rushed in.
10. The murdered man. The close proximity of the chairs and the privacy of the house (as shown in the plan) indicate this.
11. No. His bag is in the machine.
12. Yes. The position of the bags and the overcoat show this.
13. Jealousy.
14. Yes. Because of jealousy.

Mr. and Mrs. Charles Leroy, each of whom received mail, lived here. The stethoscope shows the murdered man was a physician. The absence of a doctor's plate or other sign shows he did not live here, but the red cross on the radiator of the car shows it was his machine. He parked it off the dead end street, and it was in the driveway long enough to drip a puddle; the car was probably here for the night. The initials C. L. tally with those of Charles Leroy, and the sample case, apparently carried by him also, indicates he was a traveling salesman. Since a man carries his coat on his forearm and forward of his bag, Leroy was about to enter the house; the presence of unopened mail clinches this point. Since the house is surrounded by hedges and situated on a dead end street, the people at the breakfast table, sitting extraordinarily close, like lovers, must have felt free from observation. The doctor had left his professional bag in his car, hence his visit was non-professional. Leroy dropped his bags suddenly, letting his coat drop to the ground and not even carrying his bags to the porch. He did this because he must have seen his wife on intimate terms with the doctor, who had apparently spent the night in the house. In a fit of jealousy, Leroy pulled out a gun and shot the doctor as he sought to rush from the house.

THE HENDRICKS MURDER

1. Yes. He was working quietly and peacefully when shot, because, in spite of his hot temper there is no mark of struggle.
2. No. The murderer would have to pass Hendricks to do it—and this could not be done without a struggle of which there is no evidence.
3. Yes. The opened safe indicates this.
4. No. The same shows he had valuable papers and material worth stealing.
5. No. There is no evidence to show when the murder was committed.
6. No. In order to get the gun it would have been necessary to disturb Hendricks.

7. The railroad tracks and passing trains.
8. Reading a letter.
9. No. Nothing is disturbed.
10. The nearest corner of the desk, (lower right) and shown by the line of the bullet and the mark on the wall.
11. The second shot. The clock was out of the range of the death bullet.
12. No. The clock must have been *set* to 6 P.M. and shot at to falsify the time.
13. The secretary— He had access to the gun. Hendricks would never have worked peacefully in the presence of his son. The fixing of the clock is to throw the guilt on the son.

The large safe indicates the presence of valuables; hence robbery may have been the motive. Hendricks was working quietly and peacefully when shot; despite his hot temper, there is no mark of fear or disturbance or action; he was leaning back and reading a letter. The passage of a train may well have obscured the sound of any shot. No one could have opened drawer A and taken the gun without arousing Hendricks' suspicions; hence it was taken before lunch, which is before his son reached town. The murderer must have stood at the nearest corner of the desk (lower right). He could scarcely miss at this point blank range, and the clock was well out of the line of fire. It follows that it was struck deliberately, and the only reason for so doing would be to falsify the time of the murder.

It is therefore proved that the secretary, who had access to the gun, took it, shot Hendricks without warning. Hot tempered Hosiah would never have worked peacefully in the presence of his estranged son. The secretary must then have set the clock at 6 p.m., shattered it with a bullet and gone home.

END OF A WEALTHY PLAYBOY

Solution

3. Yes, because she says he was "terribly upset and jeal."—obviously jealous (line 5).
4. June, because it is the only month of the year ending in "e" (line 1).

5. By train, because she speaks of his coming "direct from the Pennsyl-"—obviously the Pennsylvania station (line 4).

6. A hotel telephone number, because 3-5000 is apparently the part of a phone number following the name of the exchange, and because round numbers are usually reserved for large public buildings such as hotels, stations, etc.

7. Yes, because it is dated the 7th, and the letter, dated the 8th, speaks of a theatre ticket from yesterday (line 8), and because it bears the hotel number which she mentions (line 9).

8. Yes, because she speaks of her husband as terribly upset and jealous (line 5), of killing (line 11), of danger (line 12), and because she urges Ordway to go away (line 13).

9. No, because it is apparently her sister's address care of which Lovey wanted Ordway to write, and because he would surely know her address.

10. No, because she says "the butler's delivering" (line 17), and because the letter is so filled with anxiety and a feeling of haste that she would not want to lose the hours required to receive a posted letter.

11. Taxi.   12. Gossip.   13. Promise.   14. Worried.

15. Jealousy, as is apparent from the whole letter.

16. Direct convincing evidence is contained in the theatre stub. It was apparently in Lovey's evening bag (line 10), and she says her husband took it (line 10). It follows that only her husband could have brought it to Ordway's hotel room, where it must have been one of the objects for which Ordway and his murderer struggled (see statement). How Lovey's husband located Ordway from the telephone number, how they fought, and how the murderer must have escaped in too great a hurry to take the incriminating bits of paper may be conjectured.

17. Yes, because Lovey's sister can be found at 115 Wyckoff Place.

The Letter:

June 8, 1934

Gam darling,

My husband is back! He came late last night, in a taxi direct from the Pennsylvania station. He was terribly upset and jealous because of the gossip he'd heard. Luckily he doesn't know your name, but he found the stub of the theatre ticket from yesterday—the one on

which you wrote your hotel phone number—in my evening bag, and
he took it, swearing he'd find and kill the man I was with. It's terrible.
Oh, Gam, he's dangerous and hot tempered. You must promise to go
away at once. You can write me c/o my sister—Mrs. Annie Laurel,
at 115 Wyckoff Place. I'm so afraid, and simply worried to death.
I'm sending this to you by hand—the butler's delivering it —because
John mustn't find you.

Your,
Lovey

MERRILL'S ALIBI

Solution

3. Yes, because his room contains cups, medals, and athletic equipment.
4. Yes, because he was an athlete.
5. Yes, because he was an athlete.
6. Yes, because the gun rack indicates he was interested in gunnery.
7. No, because one gun is missing from the rack.
8. Yes, because it places him at his apartment at 6:45 p.m. and makes it impossible for him to have reached the Allen estate by 7:00 p.m.
9. No, because their stories are inconsistent. She says he was home until 6:45 p.m., he says he went out at six.
10. Yes, because she mentions the volume of poetry and the broken bulb. If she had merely spoken to him on the phone, he would not have been likely to speak of these two things nor she to select them as important parts of her story.
11. No. Nothing in the room is inconsistent with her story. Note that the wet umbrella, probably in the rain after 6:45 p.m. when she says he first went out, is immaterial to her version.
12. Yes, because it has been opened and folded back and is somewhat crumpled.
13. Ground floor, as shown by the height of the fence and the man, and by the fact that the light from outside, presumably from a street lamp, is cast downwards.

14. No, because Merrill lived on the ground floor and would not use the elevator.

15. At 7 : 30 p.m., because the umbrella is still wet. The puddles from it can be seen.

16. "At seven I was reading where my book is," because Merrill himself states the bulb was broken in the afternoon, and at seven on a November evening it is too dark to read by natural light. Therefore, had he been reading at seven, he would have had to sit in the chair at the right and use the lamp.

17. No. Merrill has been caught in one lie. Apparently he was with Mrs. Allen in the afternoon. Apparently she made up a story in an attempt to save him. Merrill had a motive, was a good shot and an athlete, and fabricated an alibi, which has been proved false. Doubtless he returned from the murder at about 7 : 30 p.m., arranged book and paper as if he had been reading. The paper and the bulb he may have bought any time during the afternoon. Circumstantial evidence therefore convicts him.

LUNCH ROOM MURDER

Solution

3. No, because the money has been taken neither from the counter nor the cash drawer.

4. Yes, because their three checks totaling 55 cents were rung up together on the cash register. It follows that one of them treated the other two. The fact that they sat next to each other is not convincing, although it is indicative.

5. No, because D has finished eating and has paid; A has done neither.

6. At least six—A, B, C, D, Joe and Brady.

7. Yes, because River Street, which is the only possible approach, is visible through the windows of the lunch room.

8. No. They leave no mark on a dry floor.

9. Y, because they start from near the mop which only he would be using and then proceed to the cash drawer which only he would open, except in case of robbery, which we know has not occurred in this instance.

10. No, because only his toe marks show, indicating that he ran.
11. Yes, because his footsteps (heel and toe mark) show that he walked and did not run to the cash register.
12. Near the cash register, because we know that he walked to it and ran from it, and because he did not close the cash drawer. It follows that something—namely the murder—frightened him while he was there.
13. Z, because they start at the far side of stool A.
14. Yes, because his toe marks leave via the kitchen door.
15. Yes, because their footsteps do not show and the space near the kitchen is wet.
16. Yes, because the man whose hand print appears must have stood near the mop, in the position where footprints X appear.
17. No, because the mark of his right hand appears. Therefore he held the gun in his left hand.
18. C, because he was left-handed. Cups and glasses are normally placed at the right and *are* at the right of A's, B's, and D's plates. The smears of glass and cup show C pushed these to the left where they now are. It follows that C was left-handed and the murderer.

AX ME ANOTHER

Pull rope DOWN and ax will go UP.

WHICH WAY PLEASE?

A—Up	E—Down	J—Up
B—Up	F—Down	K—Up
C—Up	G—Up	L—Down
D—Up	H—Up	M—Up
	I—Down	

THE FATAL ARGUMENT

Jack killed Fred.
Dick was not in the crowd.
The reasoning follows:
Tom could not be the murderer since he just made the acquaintance of the murdered man. He could not be the victim because he

[271]

"wouldn't dare tell." (If he had been the victim, he *couldn't* tell.) He must have been there because he knew who committed the murder.

Dick is the only one who was not there because there is nothing to indicate his presence. He is not the murderer obviously.

Harry was neither the murderer nor the victim because he stood behind the murderer when he fired the fatal shot.

Jack could have been in Philadelphia the evening of the murder and still have committed the murder, since it only takes two hours from Philadelphia to New York and the murder was committed long after midnight.

Fred must have been the victim because Jack is clearly the murderer (since he was caught two days later in the Bronx) and Tom and Harry are obviously alive. (Tom wouldn't tell and Harry was there.)

THE HOLD-UP

Curley is guilty. The reasoning follows:

Rogers must be innocent since three of his statements would be false if he were guilty (and only one statement can be false according to rule).

Rogers' one false statement is therefore "The Rat and I were in Pittsburgh on May 12th."

Looking now at The Rat's statement No. 2, we see that he says the same thing that Rogers said which we know is false. Hence all the rest of The Rat's statements must be true and he is innocent.

Now let us look at Slim's statements. Slim says Curley did it. He also says that Rogers helped Curley, which we know is not so because "I know nothing of the robbery" is one of Rogers' three true statements. It follows then that Slim's last statement is false and "Curley did it" must be true.

Curley says he is innocent. This statement obviously must be the only false one. If you examine Curley's other three statements you'll see how they can all be true.

WHO KILLED SULLIVAN?

Red is the guilty man. The reasoning follows:

Lefty's first two statements cannot both be false, hence the third

Fig. 5 is at 10:30 P.M. on July 10, 1914. Naturally no fire is burning in July. Reilly has already given up whiskey, but he's still allowed his evening cigar.

In Figures 4, 5 and 6, the Chinese vase on the mantel has been cracked and repaired. But the ornamental plate is cracked only in 5 and 6; it must have been dropped between 1912 and 1914. But Fig. 4 is in July, and there would be no fire lit, so it is obviously the lower center picture.

Figures 1, 2 and 3 are all dated Jan. 10, 1902—before the Chinese vase cracked, before Reilly's chair was patched, before the table was scratched. But these first three pictures can be told apart by the cigar, the highball and the fire. The upper right picture is Fig. 1—a full glass, a clean fire, a fresh cigar. Fig. 2 is just one minute later, the lower right—as Reilly sipped his drink, he dropped his cigar ash on the floor. Fig. 3 is 20 minutes later—the cigar has gone out, the highball is nearly finished, and the fireplace is full of ashes. This must be the upper center.

THE MARCH OF TIME

(*Solutions*)

The only possible correct order of the pictures is:

7	1
5	3
2	8
6	4

Evidence of the time-sequence is given by the chewing-gum, the right shoelace becoming untied, the length of runs in the socks, the puddle of water and foot-prints, crushing of the cigar-butt, frayed trouser-cuffs, etc.

Answers to the questions:

1. He tied his right shoelace. The *left* lace is untied in Picture No. 8.
2. He is taking shorter steps and is dragging his heels.
3. The runs in his socks and his frayed trouser-cuffs probably indicate poor quality or cheap merchandise.
4. He didn't remove the chewing-gum. He doesn't tie his shoes properly. He doesn't look where he is walking.

5. The rubber heel marks and the mark of the chewing gum.
6. No, because no shadows show in any of the pictures.
7. Because the run in the left sock is higher and another run has started near the heel.
8. Because No. 6 shows that he stepped on the cigar-butt immediately after leaving footprints in the road.
9. Because both socks have runs, his trousers are frayed, his shoes no longer shined, and quite a little rain has fallen.

WET OR DRY

1. I woke up l
2. I sat up s
3. I got up k
4. I ran the water a
5. I took a shower g
6. I grabbed a towel c
7. I dried myself r
8. I started dressing j
9. I put on my socks n
10. I put on my shoes q
11. I finished dressing p
12. I went out doors o
13. I walked in the rain m
14. I wet my shoes b
15. I went back home h
16. I dried my shoes e
17. I put on rubbers f
18. I went out again i
19. I didn't wet my shoes d

ENCLOSED PLEASE FIND

1. He received the catalogue a
2. He opened the catalogue n
3. He saw what he wanted k
4. He turned to the price list ı
5. He looked up the price g
6. He wrote for a dozen d

7. He enclosed the dollar m
8. He sealed the letter j
9. He mailed the letter e
10. He awaited the package h
11. He received the package p
12. He opened the package b
13. He counted the contents l
14. He found all twelve f
15. He tried one out o
16. He tried out a second c
17. He used up another q
18. He used every one i
19. He ordered some more s

TRUE OR FALSE?

Group A

1. True.
2. False. Water can be made to boil until it freezes by gradually exhausting the pressure in the container.
3. False. Hongkong is a province in China.
4. True. June 21st is the longest day of the year and the first day of summer.
5. False. The part near Detroit is South of the U. S.
6. False. The Bible says Jonah was swallowed by a big fish.
7. False.
8. False. There is a great deal of snow on the tops of Central African mountains.
9. False. She was Mrs. Isaac Goose of Boston.
10. False.
11. True.
12. True.
13. False. Nanking is.
14. False. It is "I."
15. False.
16. True. It is Andorra.
17. True. It weighs about 1300 lbs.
18. True.

19. False. It is about 1 degree off.
20. False. They lay eggs in the clothes and the hatching larva does the damage.
21. False. A knot is a measure of speed and not distance. It is 1 Nautical mile per hour.
22. True.
23. False. It is a mechanical universe.
24. False. Canberra is the capital.
25. True.

Group B

1. False. Cross either pole of the Earth and you accomplish this.
2. True.
3. False.
4. False. It is about 75% copper.
5. False. It does not contain Magenta or the combination of Violet and Red.
6. False.
7. False. Trotsky was not at Lenin's funeral.
8. True.
9. True.
10. False.
11. False.
12. False.
13. False. It points to the Magnetic Pole in Northern Canada.
14. False. Brazil has the larger area.
15. False. Paris is nearer Buenos Aires than El Paso is.
16. False. Only on September 21st and March 21st does the sun set in the west.
17. False. John Hansen of Maryland was elected to that office by the first congress of the confederation November 5, 1781.
18. False. Cream floats on milk.
19. False. Carson City is.
20. True.
21. True.
22. False.

23. False. One can go from Texas to Colorado and travel only 40 miles.
24. True.
25. True.

Group C

1. False. It is the capital of Honduras.
2. False. It is Key West.
3. False.
4. False. Venus is not a star.
5. False. Lief Ericson discovered America.
6. False. It was signed July 2nd 1776.
7. False. Sodium is lighter than many woods.
8. False. It is in Northern Norway.
9. True.
10. True.
11. True.
12. True.
13. True.
14. False. The century years, 1900, 1800 etc. are not leap years.
15. True. It is only 1.06 square miles in area; Greater London is 693 square miles in area.
16. False. It is colorless.
17. False. They are made of iron.
18. False. Delhi is the capital.
19. False. January 1st 1901 was the first day of the 20th Century.
20. False.
21. False. It refers to the first day of summer.
22. False. An explosion in vacuum would be noiseless.
23. True.
24. True.
25. False. She was a Greek.

Group D

1. True.
2. False.
3. False.

4. True.
5. True. The whirling wind *within a hurricane* travels very fast but the hurricane itself moves slowly.
6. False. It is the figure 8 on geographical globes.
7. False. It is a Heptagon.
8. True.
9. False.
10. False.
11. False.
12. True. He is on the Earth which travels millions of miles.
13. False. It is the decimal part of a logarithm.
14. False. It is the inner sole of a shoe.
15. False. It comes from sheep.
16. True. There is little or no atmosphere on the moon hence sound is impossible there.
17. True.
18. True.
19. True.
20. False.
21. False. It is in France.
22. True.
23. True.
24. False. They make a noise like human laughter when they are freightened.
25. False. She is the wife of an Earl.

NAME FIVE

1. Marie, Annette, Cecile, Emilie, Yvonne.
2. Huron, Erie, Ontario, Superior, Michigan.
3. Mercury, Venus, Earth, Mars, Jupiter, Saturn, Uranus, Neptune, Pluto.
4. Mozart, Beethoven, Yehudi Menuhin, Ruggiero Ricci, Josef Hoffman, Mischa Elman, Handel, Heifetz.
5. Jack Horner, Bo-Peep, Boy Blue, Miss Muffet, Tommy Tucker, Polly Flinders, Nancy Etticoat.
6. Macon, Shenandoah, Akron, Los Angeles, ZR-2, Italia, Roma, R-34, Hindenburg.

7. Tuba, Trombone, Tambourine, Triangle, Trumpet.
8. Time flies. Procrastination is the thief of time. Time will tell. There is no time like the present. There is a time and place for everything. Time and tide waiteth for no man.
9. Al, John, Adam, Sydney, F. Hopkinson, Joseph, Samuel Francis, Kirby.
10. The horse shoe, wish bone, four leaf clover, rabbit's foot, blue-bird.
11. Kangaroo. Cockatoo. Dingo. Koala. Black Swan. Wombat. Cassowary. Lyre bird.
12. Break a mirror. Spill Salt. Walk under a ladder. Open an umbrella indoors. Sit 13 at a table. Light 3 cigarettes on one match.

NAME TEN

1. Old Golds, Lucky Strikes, Chesterfields, Murads, Camels, Fatima, Phillip Morris, Tally-Ho, Egyptian Dieties, Malboro, Pall Mall, Kool.
2. Cymbal, cymbalon, cornet, cello, clarinet, castanets, clavichord, clavier, calliope, concertina, celesta, crotalum, clavecin.
3. Brazil, Colombia, Venezuela, Guiana, Ecuador, Peru, Bolivia, Argentina, Uruguay, Paraguay, Chile.
4. Ziegfeld, Count Zeppelin, Stefan Zweig, Efrem Zimbalist, Israel Zangwill, Anders Zorn, Zog, King of Albania, Ignacio Zuloaga, Heinie Zimmerman, Arnold Zweig.
5. New York, Chicago, Philadelphia, Detroit, Los Angeles, Cleveland, St. Louis, Baltimore, Boston, Pittsburgh.
6. London, New York, Tokyo, Berlin, Paris, Chicago, Moscow, Osaka, Leningrad, Buenos Aires.

GENERAL TEST

1. The letter is E and the sentence is:
   These three sewers never need new needles.
2. Say I never gave you something.
3. STRENGTHS.
4. No. 3—An even number can be a prime number. 2 is even and prime.

5. ^{4} 7534865439456328 ^{4} 34752 ^{4} 37343259879 ^{4} 24043523475632365-
$_3$ 6436234843 $_3$ $_3$

5. 7534865439456328347523734325987924043523475632365-
6436234843
6. "Smith, while I wrote 'wrote wrote,' wrote 'wrote,' " I wrote.
7. A BAD CAB
8. If a friend be a plus and an enemy be a minus then:
The enemy of the enemy is the friend
or a minus times a minus is a plus.
9. INDIVISIBILITY.
10. eau, ow, oe, ot, ew, ough, owe, oh.
11. 2 and 2.
12. ZEBRA.
13. Third cousin.
14. There is no such thing.
15. MODELS and SELDOM.
16. Verb is to sentence as vowel is to word.
17. Minute.
18. 9^{99} 1^{11}
19. Johnson is an elevator operator in the Empire State Building in New York.
20. This is impossible. A sun eclipse can never occur the day after a moonlight night.

HOW MUCH DO YOU KNOW?

Group 1

1. Tennessee Valley Authority, Citizens' Conservation Corps, National Recovery Act.
2. George Gershwin.
3. A school in New London, Texas was blown up with a loss of over 400 lives.
4. Increasing the number of Justices from 9 to 15 in the Supreme Court.
5. Polaris or the North Star.
6. Beethoven.

7. From the eighth month.
8. One of the inconceivably minute negative electrical charges inside of an atom.
9. These were the only two States which went Republican in 1936 and instead of the old slogan "As Maine goes, so goes the Nation" the Democrats adopted the new one "As Maine goes, so goes Vermont."
10. Execution of murder by strangulation.
11. Gilbert and Sullivan.
12. In Alaska.
13. Nazi Germany's union with Austria.
14. Firpo, the prize fighter.
15. Wiley Post and Will Rogers
16. Birmingham.
17. Gone With The Wind.
18. The line drawn through the focus parallel to the directrix.
19. Edna Ferber.
20. Alexander the Great.
21. Patrick Henry.
22. 20.
23. The sun moves completely around the sky parallel to the horizon never getting any higher or lower.
24. Albert Einstein.
25. Society for the Prevention of Cruelty to Animals.

Group 2

1. Nazi Germany.
2. Somerset Maugham.
3. The Seventeenth Century.
4. William Howard Taft.
5. In stagnant swamps and ponds.
6. In the same place as.
7. 13.
8. Maine.
9. As a test for an acid.
10. 98.6 F.
11. No. It is in the center of the North Atlantic Ocean.

12. Progression by fifths in harmony.
13. Marie Antoinette.
14. "At long last."
15. The Loyalists.
16. P. T. Barnum.
17. A $100,000 bill.
18. Liége, Belgium.
19. Milton.
20. Lord Protector of England in the 17th Century.
21. The Polish Corridor.
22. A lullaby.
23. Edith Wharton.
24. The reason for being.
25. One who writes for another anonymously.

Group 3

1. Bach, Beethoven and Brahms.
2. May 23rd, 1937.
3. Tokio, Japan.
4. A mark under the letter c to indicate the sound of s.
5. A marriage between a royal male personage and a woman of inferior rank in which titles and estates of husband are not shared by children.
6. American poet and humorist.
7. Teheran.
8. Helsinki.
9. A railed seat on the back of an elephant.
10. A character in Gilbert and Sullivan's opera "Mikado."
11. Madagascar.
12. The ratio of the weight of a body to the weight of an equal volume of water.
13. The power by which a State takes land or property for public necessity regardless of the wish of the owner.
14. Right off French Guiana in South America.
15. J. M. Barrie.
16. 2.54 centimeters.
17. A triangle, two of whose sides are equal.
18. Platinum.

19. A Japanese method of committing suicide.
20. June 28, 1919.
21. Webster.
22. Between New York State and Canada, in the St. Lawrence River.
23. When one side has scored more than 100 points.
24. A Canadian doctor, who brought the Quintuplets into the world.
25. Arsenic.

Group 4

1. North of Poland.
2. Doe.
3. A musical instrument.
4. About 35,000 feet.
5. Harry Weiss.
6. Andromeda.
7. South.
8. Orange, lemon, grapefruit, lime.
9. A fish.
10. A race created by Richard Wagner, in his operas "The Ring of the Niebelungs."
11. The College of Cardinals.
12. Woodrow Wilson.
13. The curve taken by a loose rope or chain suspended between two supports.
14. Ivan Kreuger.
15. Newton D. Baker.
16. Frederick Chopin.
17. National Youth Administration.
18. Venice.
19. 1,200,000.
20. Old Gold cigarettes—P. Lorillard, manufacturer.
21. A device for regulating temperature.
22. An instructor in public speaking and personality and author of "How to Win Friends and Influence People," and "Five Minute Biographies."

23. A machine used by mechanics for making parts of other machines.
24. Chicago.
25. The Mantelpiece (from the Bab Ballads of W. S. Gilbert).

PART V—PENCIL AND PAPER GAMES
4. CONCENTRATION

~~Washington~~ New York ~~Boston~~
~~Toledo~~ ~~Omaha~~
Denver Cincinnati

10. GEOGRAPHY

1. Roumania
2. Norway
3. Belgium
4. Siberia
5. Germany
6. Chili
7. Russia
8. Haiti
9. Alaska
10. Palestine

15. YOU SEE BUT YOU DON'T OBSERVE

1. To the right
2. Benjamin Franklin
3. 2¾ inches
4. 6⅛ inches
5. 20
6. 8½ by 11 inches
7. To your left (counterclockwise)
8. 4
9. The Lincoln Memorial
10. 2 inches
11.
12. 7½ inches
13. slightly bent
14. Yes
15. No.
16. There is no 6 there
17. Sometimes
18. G H I in New York
19. Left
20. 4 feet 8½ inches
21. White
22. Front
23. 12
24. 1 inch

16. ADVERTISING SLOGAN CONTEST

1. Woodbury soap
2. Fisk Tires
3. Palmolive soap
4. Packard Automobile
5. Camel cigarettes
6. Bon Ami
7. Old Gold cigarettes
8. Ivory soap
9. Maxwell House coffee
10. Chesterfield cigarettes
11. Paris garters
12. Grapenuts
13. Armour ham
14. Prudential Life Insurance Co.
15. Buick
16. Pompeian face cream
17. Victor talking machines
18. Steinway pianos
19. Castoria
20. Terminal Barber shops.

17. ANAGRAMS

1. Cafés
2. Later
3. Voter
4. Aside
5. Rouge
6. Shame
7. Brace
8. Raffle
9. Yield
10. Gusto
11. Types
12. Gavel
13. Begets
14. Verity
15. Swivel
16. Garden
17. Appeal
18. Diners
19. Garnet
20. Gnomes

21. BIOGRAPHIES: Beethoven

25. GENERAL QUIZ GAME

1. Helena.
2. Thackeray.
3. Native of India employed as a soldier by a European power.
4. June 28, 1919.
5. Italy.
6. A columnist on the World Telegram.
7. The outside of the glass does not expand as quickly as the inside.
8. None is here.
9. Hardin County, Kentucky.
10. Richard Wagner.
11. The 8 on a geographical globe.
12. 3⅜
13. An order to produce the body.
14. Northwest.
15. Spanish lace cape, worn by women.

16. 4 degrees centigrade.
17. A small musical instrument.
18. Yankees.
19. 11.
20. Bully tree or the sapodilla.
21. Government detective.
22. Point directly down in the opposite direction from the zenith, which is directly overhead.
23. John W. Davis.
24. Independence of women in retaining of their maiden names.
25. 29,000 feet.

PART VIII—MAGIC AND STUNTS
FAKE BETS

1. Tilt the hat over to the side so that the glass of liquid is still under it. Suck liquid out through a straw.
2. The thing you hold in your hand is an ice cube in a handkerchief. You can hold this comfortably for three minutes, and if anyone wants to try it, hand him the cube without the handkerchief.
3. You can, if you just put uncooked dry coffee in the cup.
4. This is done by placing the egg in an old fashioned egg cup and blowing very hard at the bottom of the egg, causing air to get in between the egg and the cup and turn the egg around.
5. Of course you can. If you keep on handing him the pack of cards long enough, he is bound to receive the card he is thinking of. In handing him the full pack, you are naturally including his card, and hence living up to your claim.
6. If you draw a circle of chalk around the top of a man's pants you will be drawing a circle around him which he will not dare to get out of.
7. One person is on one side of the door and the other is on the other side. Both people leaning against the door.
8. Open up a walnut, show the nut to your audience, then eat the nut.
9. Put two crackers under two different hats, eat both crackers and then put each hat on separately. The eaten objects (crackers) will, of course, be under the two hats.
10. Name a horse.